For Grandpa:
Teacher, Mentor, Friend

A Note to Parents:

Dear Parents,

Recently my eight-year-old son came to me and proudly announced, "Mom, I read the whole *Book of Mormon!*" I knew that he had been reading each night, but I was surprised that he had finished the entire book. I asked, "What was your favorite part, Jared?" He said, "The Joseph Smith stuff." Surprised, I asked, "What Joseph Smith stuff?" He answered, "You know, the part where he sees the angel and gets the golden plates."

Suddenly I knew what had happened. "Jared, did you read all of the chapters that were called 'Section 1', 'Section 2', and so on?" He replied, "Yeah. That part was pretty boring, but I wanted to read the whole book, so I read it anyway." This diligent child had read and read until he finished the entire volume, including the *Doctrine and Covenants* and the *Pearl of Great Price*! This was a monumental accomplishment for such a young boy, but it demonstrated a fundamental lack of understanding: He couldn't comprehend enough to know when one book ended and the next one began. He was so eager to learn and obey that he persevered, even though he received almost no benefits for his diligence.

That's the reason for this book. Our wonderful children are eager to learn, and it is our responsibility to provide them with every opportunity. This book is a tool to aid you in helping your child acquire the vocabulary and reading skills necessary to read the *Book of Mormon*.

To accomplish this, we have used the "pyramid" approach to learning: We build a solid foundation of simple vocabulary and gradually add layers of new concepts so that the child actually learns to read the scriptures as he reads the book. Our goal is to teach enough scripture vocabulary that by the time the child reaches "Third Nephi", he can read the words of Christ without needing simplification.

We hope that this book will be a valuable tool in your "parenting toolbox". If you have any questions or comments, please contact us at jstapp@gte.net or in care of:

Jolynne Stapp
PO Box 962
Londonderry, NH 03053

Book of Mormon Reader

For Young Book of Mormon Readers

Illustrated by Becki Berrett

Retold by Jolynne Berrett Stapp

ISBN #0-88042-036-7

Lehi Leaves Jerusalem

1 Nephi 1-2

Lehi lived in Jerusalem 600 years before Jesus was born. He had a nice house and a beautiful family. His wife's name was Sariah. They had four sons: Laman, Lemuel, Sam, and Nephi. Lehi was a good man who tried to do what he knew was right.

One day while Lehi was praying, he had a vision. In his vision, Jerusalem was destroyed. The Lord was going to punish the city. The people who lived there were very wicked.

Lehi tried to tell the people what the Lord had said. The people laughed and told him to go away. He tried again and again to teach them. They became angry and tried to hurt him.

Soon after that, the Lord told Lehi to leave Jerusalem. Bad people were coming to kill him unless he left the city.

Lehi and Sariah quickly gathered what they would need for their family. They took their tent, some food, and a few animals. They had to leave their house, gold, silver, and other things behind. They were very sad as they left the beautiful city.

Lehi and his family fled to the south until they came to the Red Sea. There they found a valley with fresh water to drink. Lehi named this valley the "Valley of Lemuel".

What would you do if the Lord told you to leave your home quickly?

What would you take with you?

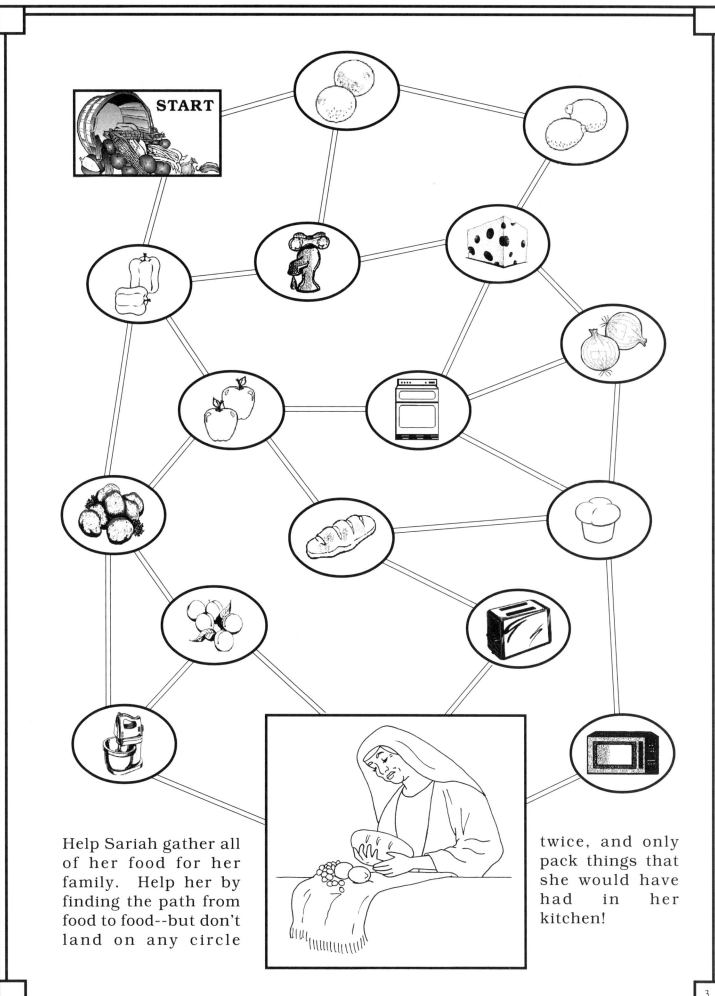

START

Help Sariah gather all of her food for her family. Help her by finding the path from food to food--but don't land on any circle twice, and only pack things that she would have had in her kitchen!

The Brass Plates

1 Nephi 3-4

The Lord came again to Lehi in a dream. He told Lehi that they had left something very important in Jerusalem. They had left their family history and their scriptures. The Lord told them to go back and get the precious book.

In those days, all books had to be written by hand. Lehi's family history, or genealogy, was written on thin sheets of brass. This meant that the book would last a long time. It also meant that the book would have cost a lot of money to make.

Since this copy of Lehi's genealogy was written on sheets of brass, it was called the "Brass Plates".

Lehi's family history was special, because Lehi was a Jew. The Jewish history was the book which we know today as the Old Testament. Lehi needed to take his scriptures, which contained his family history, with him into the wilderness.

A man named Laban had the Brass Plates. Laban was Lehi's cousin. He was not a nice man, and Lehi's sons were afraid of him. They did not want to go back to Jerusalem. They were afraid to ask him for the valuable book.

Nephi had more faith than his brothers. He said, "I will go. If the Lord wants me to do it, He will help me do

it." When Nephi said this, the other brothers decided to go, too.

When the brothers reached Jerusalem, they decided that Laman should ask Laban for the book. When Laman did this, Laban became very angry and tried to hurt him. Laman escaped and ran back to his brothers. When they heard his story, they were afraid.

Again Nephi had faith. He told the others, "We need to obey the Lord. He will help us."

Nephi decided to go back to Laban and try again to get the book. He and his brothers went to their old house and got some of the gold, sil-

ver, and other valuable things the family had left behind. Then they went to Laban's house and tried to trade the valuables for the book.

Laban took the gold and silver, but he would not give Nephi the Brass Plates. Nephi went back to his brothers and told them what had happened. Now they didn't have the book or the treasures, and they were very sad.

The brothers wanted to go back to their mother and father. Nephi would not leave. He said that they had to try again. He did not know what to do next, but he knew that the Lord would help him if he kept trying to obey.

He prayed for help. The Lord told him what to do. When he got close to Laban's house, he saw a man asleep in the street. Nephi went closer to the man and saw that he was Laban. The Lord told him to kill Laban and use his clothes for a disguise.

Nephi did not want to do this. The Lord told him again that he must kill Laban. That was the only way to get the Brass Plates. Lehi's family needed the book before they could do the other things the Lord wanted them to do.

After killing Laban, Nephi put on Laban's clothes. He tried to look just like Laban. He went to the house and spoke to Laban's servant in Laban's voice. The servant was fooled and led Nephi to the room where the Brass Plates were kept.

Nephi took the book and ran back to his brothers. They were very happy. Nephi was happy, too. He thanked the Lord for helping him find a way to obey.

_____

Why were Laman and Lemuel afraid?

Why wasn't Nephi afraid?

What does this story teach us?

What can we do when we are afraid?

Can You Break the Code?

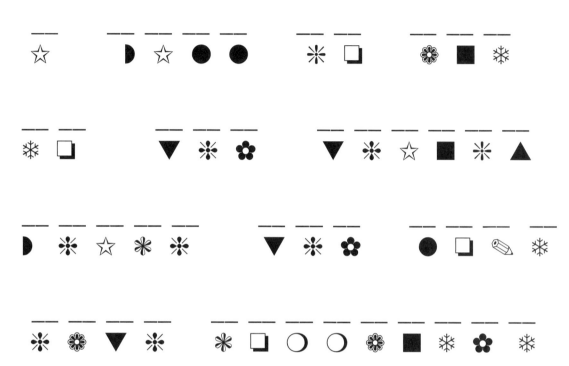

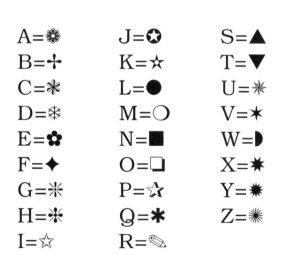

A=❋ J=✪ S=▲
B=✢ K=☆ T=▼
C=✳ L=● U=✳
D=❊ M=○ V=✶
E=✿ N=■ W=◗
F=◆ O=▢ X=✻
G=✳ P=☆ Y=✺
H=✳ Q=✸ Z=✳
I=☆ R=✏

Lehi's Dream

1 Nephi 8-9

Lehi had another dream. In this dream, Heavenly Father showed him many wonderful things.

In the dream, Lehi followed an angel to a dark, empty place. Lehi was scared and decided to pray. He asked Heavenly Father to help him.

After the prayer, Lehi saw a beautiful tree. It had white fruit hanging from its branches. Lehi ate one of the fruits. The fruit was so delicious that Lehi's soul filled with joy.

Lehi wanted to give some of the fruit to his family, but he could not find them. He looked for them.

As he looked, he saw a river near the tree. He looked along the river and saw Sariah with Sam and Nephi. They were standing where the river began. Lehi called to them, and they came and ate some of the fruit.

Lehi wanted Laman and Lemuel to eat some of the fruit, too. He looked until he found them. He told them about the fruit, but they would not come to eat it.

Lehi saw a large group of people standing at the beginning of the river. They were trying to walk along a path at the edge of the river. Some of them got lost in a dark cloud which hid part of the path.

Some of the people walked through the cloud and were not lost. Lehi watched those people and saw that they were holding onto an iron rod which ran along the path. The iron rod helped them walk through the dark cloud to the tree. There they ate the fruit.

Lehi heard a noise. He turned and saw a large building on the other side of the river. The building was filled with people. These people were laughing and making fun of the people who were eating the fruit.

Some of the people eating the fruit listened to the people in the building. They left the tree and joined the laughing people in the building.

Lehi told his family about his dream. They did not understand what the dream meant.

What was the iron rod?

What do you think Lehi's dream meant?

How could you find out?

Scrambled Words

What did Lehi see in his dream?
Unscramble the words to find out.

lgnae   __ __ __ __ __

erte   __ __ __ __

iturf   __ __ __ __ __

rrvei   __ __ __ __ __

lcudo   __ __ __ __ __

idoorrn   __ __ __ __ | __ __ __

ngdbilui   __ __ __ __ __ __ __ __

Nephi's Vision

1 Nephi 10-15

Nephi wanted to understand his father's dream. He knew that Heavenly Father answers prayers, so he decided to pray for understanding.

After Nephi finished praying, he saw the vision, too. In this vision, an angel showed him all of the things that Lehi had seen. The angel also told him what the dream meant.

When Nephi asked about the tree, the angel showed him visions of Jesus' life. He told Nephi that the tree was a symbol of the Love of God, which Jesus would share with the world.

Nephi also learned that the iron rod represented the Word of God, which is the Gospel.

The river stood for the wickedness of the world, and the dark cloud stood for the teachings of Satan.

The large building was filled with the people who did not believe in the Gospel. These people were proud and wicked. They tried to get the good people to come into the building. They wanted to turn the good people into bad people.

The good people walked along the path and held onto the iron rod. This meant that they "held on" to the Word of God to help get through the dark clouds of their lives. The Gospel helps us get through the bad times when we need help. Also, the Gospel helps us to be happy and peaceful when times are good.

When the good people got to the tree, they ate the fruit and were happy. This meant that they shared the Love of God. God loved them for doing what was right. They were happy when they knew that Heavenly Father loved them.

What did the tree stand for?

What was the iron rod?

How can you hold onto the iron rod?

How do you know that Heavenly Father loves you, too?

Connect the Boxes

Match the picture to the idea it represents.

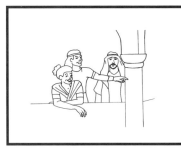

The Word of God
(the Gospel)

The people who
did not believe
in the Gospel

The wickedness
of the world

Good people who
held on to the
iron rod, or lived
the Gospel

The Love of God,
which Jesus would
teach to the world

The teachings
of Satan

In the Wilderness

1 Nephi 16, 17

The Lord told Lehi to take his family even farther into the wilderness. This meant that they were going even farther into the desert, where there were not very many plants or animals. There were no people at all, except for Lehi's family. Lehi did not know which direction to go.

The Lord helped him. One morning Lehi found a round brass ball. It was sitting on the ground in front of his tent door. The ball had two spindles, or pointers, to show Lehi which direction to travel. Lehi called this ball a "liahona".

One day, Nephi's bow broke. Now he had no way to hunt for animals to feed his family. Everyone was afraid that they were going to starve. He did not know what to do. So he knelt down and prayed for help.

The Lord caused writing to appear on the Liahona. This writing told Nephi where to find the materials he needed for a new bow. He was able to feed his family again.

Lehi's family spent eight years in the wilderness. As long as they were faithful and obedient, the Liahona guided them. When they were bad, the Liahona didn't work. Heavenly Father was trying to teach them (and us) to obey.

_____

What does this story teach us about prayer?

Coloring Fun

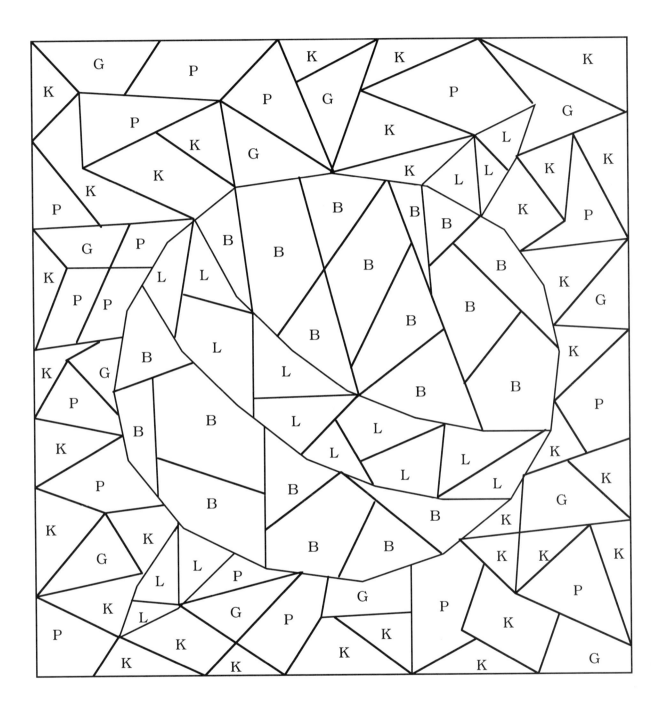

Color each space the color which matches the letters listed below. What do you see?

L = Light Brown
G = Green
K = Blue

B = Brown
P = Purple

Nephi Builds a Boat

1 Nephi 17-18

Lehi and his family travelled several years through the sand, rocks, and mountains of Arabia until they arrived at the ocean. They found a beautiful valley on the seashore with many trees. Lehi named this valley "Bountiful", which means "land of plenty."

The Lord spoke to Nephi and told him to build a boat. Nephi did not know how to build a boat, but he didn't worry. He knew that Heavenly Father would help him.

Nephi prayed and asked, "Where can I go to get the things I will need for the boat?" Heavenly Father showed him where to go. He also showed Nephi how the boat should be built.

Laman and Lemuel laughed at Nephi. They said, "You don't know how to build a boat!" Nephi ignored them and kept working.

Laman and Lemuel teased Nephi for many days. Nephi said, "If God commands me to do anything, I can do it. If He tells me to turn this water into dirt, I can do it. If

He can do these miracles, why do you think He can't show me how to build a simple boat?"

Laman and Lemuel could tell that Nephi spoke the truth, and they could not argue with him any more.

It was not easy to build the boat. The Lord wanted Nephi to put the pieces together in unusual ways. Nephi had never seen that way of building, and many times he had to ask for help. He often went into the mountains to pray, and Heavenly Father taught him many great things.

Finally the boat was finished. Even Laman and Lemuel were impressed. Nephi had done a good job building it. The ship was big and strong.

The Lord told Lehi to take his family and all of their belongings onto the boat. They gathered food, seeds, and other things to take with them. They knew that they might be in the boat for a long time.

Could you have built the boat?

Who would have helped you?

What would you take on the boat?

Word Search

```
O D I N G Z L L E G Y N P T T H X X F I
M H D T S T O R M C W T D N Y V G N R S
M K N P P D D L R M A N S L Q A D O I U
N M I P U N T I E W M E A W C E N L S Z
H B O R G N R E E C F N I U Y L R Y Z A
M R N O O M T A G K N I L R E P E N T U
O F Z M Z V O A L B Y T I L H J A B P Q
I K S I T K X L U T D N N R N V U N A Y
D X I S G Q T N F S M O G R Y W K Y I Y
D K A E C C M R K O Z C N Y Z C O P N L
F Q Y D Q R V O N L B N D E G R B H P K
Z N B L H Z G B A L Y A O P S H Y J N H
K B L A Y S D B H U S C Y R U I B O A T
E F R N I R O U T K U I U A U G B B L H
R D C D M C E T V V R R P Y T D K U R N
Y V W K W T O S P W Z E T I K E A N V H
H L P I R D X B J C B M I T X L Y B X E
C D I J H W U M G F P A O B I Q L Q H J
L U F U D I N E E Q I D H R D C D H M T
K V C V O A S S A F E X C D B B N U U T
```

Untie

Promised Land

Safe

Storm

American Continent

Stubborn

Boat

Thankful

Repent

Sailing

Pray

What Do You Think?

Nephi says that the Liahona was a ". . .round ball of curious workmanship; and it was of fine brass. And within the ball were two spindles. . ." (1 Nephi 16:10)

We do not know exactly what the Liahona looked like. What do you think? Use your imagination and draw the Liahona in the box above.

Sailing to the Promised Land

1 Nephi 18

At first, the voyage was exciting. After many weeks at sea, however, everyone became restless and bored. Laman and Lemuel and their wives began to complain. They started saying mean things about Lehi and Nephi.

Nephi tried to calm them down. He told them that what they were doing was wrong. They did not want to hear this. They became very angry.

Laman and Lemuel tied Nephi up with strong ropes. Nephi could not move. Laman and Lemuel were very mean to him.

Then Laman and Lemuel noticed something strange. The Liahona was not working. It usually pointed the way they should go, but it wasn't working any more.

Laman and Lemuel were frightened. They did not know which direction to steer the ship. Then the wind started to blow. It blew harder and harder. The waves rocked the boat back and forth. As the wind increased, the waves got higher and higher.

The storm lasted for four days. Everyone was very scared. They knew that Heavenly Father was not happy with them. But they were stubborn and would not untie Nephi.

Finally the storm got so bad that they were afraid the ship would sink. Laman and Lemuel untied Nephi and repented of the awful things they had done to him.

Nephi fell to his knees and prayed for help. Immediately the storm stopped and the Liahona began pointing the way for them.

They sailed for many more days, and they did not fight any more. The Lord protected them, and soon they landed in the Promised Land, the American Continent. Here there were lots of good things to eat and safe places to live.

Lehi and his family were very thankful that the Lord had taken them to such a wonderful place.

What caused the storm?

Why did the Liahona stop working?

What made it work again?

Crossword

The answers to these questions can be found in any of the stories about Lehi's family.

ACROSS

1. The Land Bountiful was very _____.

2. Sariah packed clothes and _____ for her family.

3. One of Nephi's brothers.

4. Lehi's family stayed in the boats for a long _____.

5. Nephi often went into the _____ to pray.

6. When Nephi's brothers weren't happy, they did this.

7. _____ _____ taught Nephi great things when he prayed.

8. "I will ____ and do the things which the Lord hath commanded."

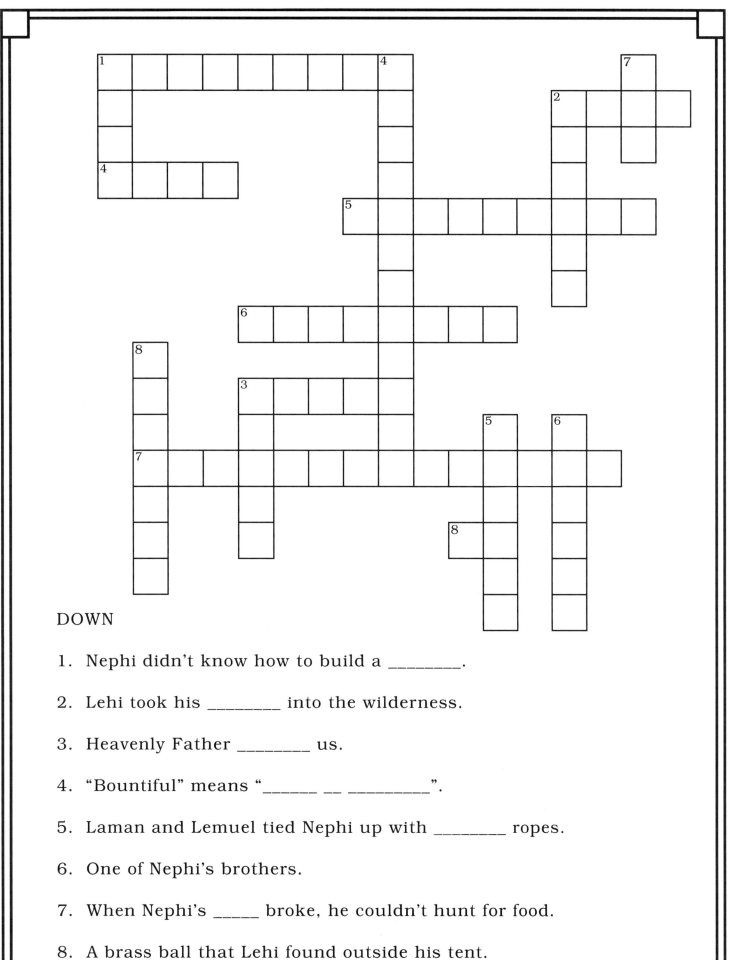

DOWN

1. Nephi didn't know how to build a _____.

2. Lehi took his _____ into the wilderness.

3. Heavenly Father _____ us.

4. "Bountiful" means "_____ __ _____".

5. Laman and Lemuel tied Nephi up with _____ ropes.

6. One of Nephi's brothers.

7. When Nephi's _____ broke, he couldn't hunt for food.

8. A brass ball that Lehi found outside his tent.

Jacob Teaches Sherem

Jacob 1, 7

Nephi was the prophet for many years. He taught his people how to build houses and temples. He taught them how to make metal tools and how to plant crops. He received revelation from Heavenly Father and used it to lead his people, who were called "Nephites".

Laman and Lemuel didn't want to work hard. They took their families and moved to another part of the land. As their families grew, they became known as "Lamanites". They lived off the land and became a wild, fierce people.

Jacob became the prophet when Nephi grew old and died. He was Nephi's younger brother. He was born while Lehi's family lived in the wilderness, before they came to the American Continent. Like Nephi and Lehi, Jacob taught the Nephites that one day Christ would come to the earth.

There was a man named Sherem who did not believe what Jacob taught. Sherem was very smart. He knew how to use words in tricky ways so that he could win any argument. He taught the people that there would not be a Christ, and the people believed him.

Jacob tried to teach Sherem the truth. Sherem asked, "How can you know what will happen in the future? How could you know that there will be a Christ?"

Instead of directly answering the question, Jacob asked, "Do you believe the scriptures?" Sherem said, "Yes."

Jacob replied, "Then you do not understand them. Every prophet has spoken or written about Christ."

Sherem still didn't believe. He demanded, "Show me a sign." He wanted Jacob to prove that he had the power of God. Jacob said, "I don't ask God for signs. If He wants you to have a sign, then let Him strike you down for a sign."

When he finished speaking, Sherem fell to the ground. Heavenly Father had made him so weak that he could not move. He stayed that way for many days.

Sherem told the people to gather around him, because he had something to say to them. He was afraid that he was going to die soon, and he wanted to tell them that he had been wrong.

He confessed to the people. He admitted that he had lied to God. He had not believed the scriptures. He had been wrong, and Heavenly Father had proved it to him. Then Sherem died.

The people heard his words and were convinced that the scriptures were true. The Spirit of the Lord was so strong in them that they fell to the ground also.

Jacob rejoiced. Peace and the love of God were restored to his people. They started reading their scriptures and keeping the commandments again.

Who were the Nephites and Lamanites?

What didn't Sherem understand?

What has every prophet said?

What did Jacob say to Sherem?

Skip every other letter around the circle to find out.

Start Here
↓

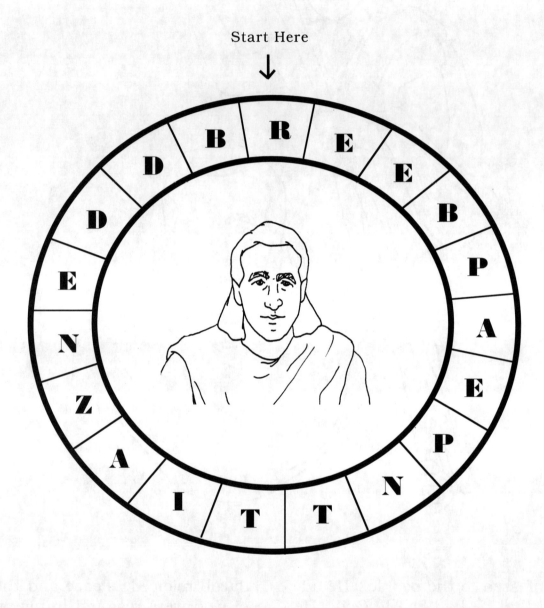

—— —— —— —— ——

—— —— ——

—— —— ——

Enos Prays

Enos

Enos was Jacob's son. Jacob taught him to keep the commandments. Jacob also taught him about eternal life and the blessings that come from making good choices.

Enos wanted to know more. He went into the forest and knelt down to pray. He prayed that Heavenly Father would forgive his sins. He wanted an answer so much that he prayed for the entire day and into the night.

At last a voice said to Enos, "Your sins are forgiven, and you will be blessed because you have so much faith." Enos knew that God could not lie, and so he was happy.

Then Enos started praying for his people, the Nephites. He heard the voice again. It said, "The Nephites will be blessed if they keep the commandments."

Then Enos prayed for the Lamanites. The Lamanites were mean to the Nephites and tried to kill them. By praying for them, Enos was praying for his enemies.

God told him that He would bless the Lamanites if they would live righteously. The Lamanites would not be destroyed. Some time in the future, the Lamanites would be taught the true Gospel of Jesus.

Enos asked Heavenly Father to keep the Nephites' history safe, even if the Lamanites killed the Nephites. Heavenly Father told him, "I will do what you ask, because you have so much faith."

Heavenly Father kept His promise. The Book of Mormon is the Nephites' history, and Heavenly Father kept it safe so that we could have it today.

Could you pray for an entire day?

What would you say that would take so much time?

Why do we have the Book of Mormon today?

What's the Secret Message?

Use the words below to fill in the blanks.

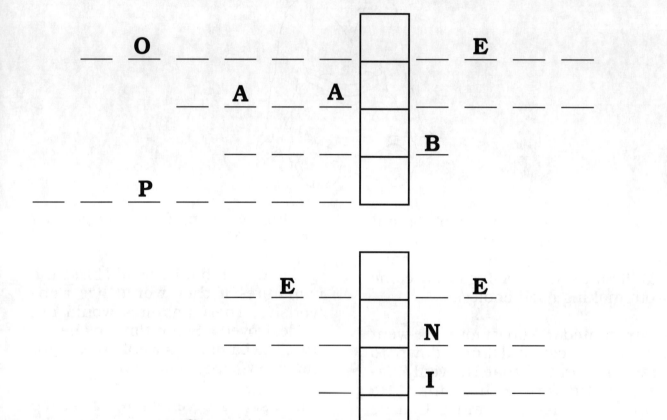

Eternal

Lamanites

Jacob

History

Blessings

Forgiveness

Faith

Nephites

People

King Noah

Mosiah 11-22

King Noah ruled the Land of Lehi-Nephi. His city had high walls all around it, because it was near the home of the Lamanites. The Lamanites did not like the Nephites and often tried to hurt them. The walls kept the Lamanites from coming into the city to attack the people who lived there.

King Noah did not want to keep the commandments. He did whatever he wanted to do. Sometimes the things he did made him happy, but they made other people sad.

He told his people to do things which broke many commandments. Soon his city was full of bad people who tried to steal from each other and hurt each other. Lehi-Nephi was not a happy place to live.

King Noah made his people pay huge taxes so that he could be rich. This made the people even more unhappy. They worked hard for their money.

King Noah took this money and spent it on fancy clothes and big parties. He had many wives, and each wore

fine clothes and ate fancy foods. His high priests also had lots of wives who needed fancy clothes and foods.

The king made his men build him a huge new palace. In the middle of the palace was his throne. It was built of the finest wood. It was covered with gold and silver decorations.

The king had a new temple built. It also was built of expensive things. The workmen used fine woods, copper, and brass to decorate it.

Noah's workers built a tall, tall tower near the temple. When the king stood on the tower, he could see his entire kingdom.

The king had lots of new buildings built. All of this was very expensive, and the people had to pay for it.

The poor people! Some of them thought that their king was right to live this way. Some of them thought he should change. But everyone agreed that the king spent a LOT of money.

Why were the people of Lehi-Nephi unhappy?

Why did King Noah want so much money?

Scrambled Picture

Copy this page onto cardstock. Cut the pieces apart and arrange them so that they make sense. What do you see?

Abinadi Teaches the King

Mosiah 11

Heavenly Father had a prophet who lived in the Land of Lehi-Nephi. His name was Abinadi. He was not happy with King Noah.

Abinadi went through the city telling the people that the Lord wanted them to repent. If they did not repent, the Lord would punish them.

The people did not think they were doing anything wrong. Noah and his high priests had told them that they were living the right way. They wanted Abinadi to go away.

Abinadi kept teaching. The people got more and more angry. Finally King Noah heard what was happening. He was angry that Abinadi said he needed to repent. He was the king! Who was this man to say what the king should do?

He said, "Bring him here so that I can kill him. He is trying to cause trouble in my kingdom."

The king's men tried to find Abinadi, but the Lord helped him escape. He hid far from the city for a long time.

Abinadi knew that he had to try to keep the people from being destroyed. He put on a disguise and went back to the city. No one knew who he was.

He tried again to teach the people to repent. He told them that the Lord was going to punish them by making the land not grow food. Hail, strong winds, and swarms of insects would come to ruin the crops. The people would have nothing to eat if they didn't do what the Lord wanted them to do.

Did the people listen? No! Instead, they got angry with Abinadi and tied him up. They carried him before King Noah. They told Noah what Abinadi had been saying.

King Noah was angry, too. He had his men cast Abinadi into prison. Then the king and his priests held a meeting. They needed to decide what to do about this trouble-maker, Abinadi.

After the meeting, Abinadi was brought back into the room. The high priests asked him some hard questions. They wanted to trick him into saying something silly, so that the people would laugh at him and not believe him.

Instead, Abinadi answered all of their questions correctly. He never made a mistake. He taught them about Heavenly Father and Jesus Christ. He taught with the Spirit. No one could argue against him.

He said, "You are angry with me because you know I am telling the truth. A lie can not hurt you as badly as the truth can."

The king became even more angry than before. He ordered his soldiers to take Abinadi and kill him.

Most of Noah's wicked priests were happy that Abinadi would no longer bother them, but one of them believed Abinadi. His name was Alma.

One of the wicked priests was named Amulon. He disagreed with Alma. He thought Alma should be punished. The more he thought about this, the more he hated Alma.

Alma begged the king to spare Abinadi's life. The king got mad at Alma and ordered him to be arrested, too. But Alma ran away from the soldiers and hid for three days. While he was hiding, he wrote down all of Abinadi's teachings.

King Noah told Abinadi, "I will give you one last chance. I will let you live if you tell me that you were lying."

Abinadi said, "I can't say that. I told you what the Lord told me to say. I cannot and will not deny that."

King Noah had his guards take Abinadi and put him to death. Abinadi never denied what he knew to be true. Because his testimony was so strong, he had the strength to stand up against the people who wanted to kill him. He was a brave, honorable man.

_____

Why was Noah so angry at Abinadi?

Why did Alma believe, when no one else did?

Word Search

```
W P D W K C I R T Y A H Z X X
C J W L N S B W Y M Q J O D R
L I A N D O K T S E I R P Y I
G S R E I D L O S O Q C T K K
X C F I D A N I B A L P P E Q
K I N J Y V S Y X B F W A N D
X B R A V E H K E A J E B Z V
O A F T I H P E N I H E L S P
U A X D C T N E P E R J E J T
P H J H N Z M O D G N I K Y B
F T Z P T E S T I M O N Y X Y
A L Z M P P R I S O N E R A N
M D E V E I L E B W C P D P O
L Q Q H J Z N Y F Q A E I L A
A P E S C A P E S X R H N H H
```

Lehi-Nephi	Trick
Abinadi	Soldiers
Repent	Escape
Noah	Alma
Kingdom	Believed
Prisoner	Testimony
Priest	Brave

Alma Is Converted

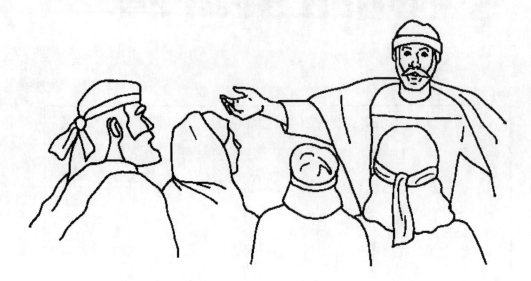

Mosiah 18

Alma studied the words of Abinadi. He prayed about them. He knew they were true. He repented of his sins.

He began to teach the people about Abinadi's teachings. He could teach only a few people at a time. They had to keep these meetings secret, because they didn't want King Noah to find out. They were afraid the king would kill them because of their beliefs.

Alma and his followers went into the woods to meet. They went to a place at the edge of the kingdom called "Mormon". Wild animals lived there. The rest of the people were scared of the animals and would not go there. Alma knew that was the safest place to meet secretly.

Alma taught the people about Jesus Christ. He taught them about baptism and repentance. He told them that they needed to take care of each other. They needed to become followers of Christ and keep the commandments.

All of the people who heard his message wanted to be baptized. Alma asked, "Are you sure this is what you want to do?"

The people clapped their hands for joy and said, "This is the desire of our hearts!"

There was a small pool of water nearby called the "Waters of Mormon". Alma took the people one by one into the water and baptized them. Two hundred and four people were baptized that day!

They called themselves the Church of Christ after that day. Alma's followers kept the commandments and were very happy.

Why were Alma's people happy?

Can you decode this?

What were the sweetest words Alma heard on his mission?
Fill in the blanks and find out.

A = (note)   H = (caboose)   N = (footprints)   U = (falcon)

B = (strawberry)   I = (waves)   O = (eye)   V = (chair)

C = (grapes)   J = (train engine)   P = (knife)   W = (window)

D = (television)   K = (crab)   Q = (column)   X = (flower)

E = (building)   L = (tree)   R = (tower)   Y = (flower)

F = (skateboard)   M = (eye)   S = (envelope)   Z = (rose)

G = (train car)   T = (building)

Discovered!

Mosiah 18

King Noah knew that something was happening in his city. There was something strange going on, but he didn't know what.

He sent spies throughout the land. He hated secrets! (At least, secrets that weren't his.)

His spies came back with news. Alma and his followers had been seen meeting in the woods by the Waters of Mormon.

The king was very angry. He sent his army out to arrest Alma and his people.

But Alma found out about the king's plans. He and his followers quickly packed food and clothing. They gathered their families and ran away from the city.

The king's army could not catch them. They ran for days and days. Finally they decided that they could stop. They found a nice place to live. They built their own little city where they could worship Heavenly Father in safety.

Why was King Noah so angry?

What did Alma and his people do when they finally stopped running?

Help Alma Escape from Noah's Soldiers

This is a fun game to play with two people or two teams. One person or team is Alma, and the other is Noah's soldiers.

Copy this page onto cardstock and cut out the playing pieces, or use a nickel for Alma and 12 pennies for the soldiers.

Object of the game: Be the only one left on the board.

To Play: Put one of the soldier pieces on each gray circle. Put the Alma piece on the black circle. The gray circles then become normal playing positions, just like the white circles. The pieces move from circle to circle in the same ways that checkers pieces move from square to square.

Alma moves from one circle to the next, unless he is able to jump over a soldier. He can only jump over one soldier at a time. Alma captures the soldier by jumping over it. If he captures all of the soldiers, he wins the game.

The soldiers can move only one circle at a time. They CAN NOT skip over circles or jump over other pieces. They capture Alma by surrounding him. When there is no way for Alma to move WITHOUT JUMPING, the soldiers win the game. (Alma cannot jump over any soldiers if the soldiers have him completely surrounded. This is the only time that Alma cannot jump.)

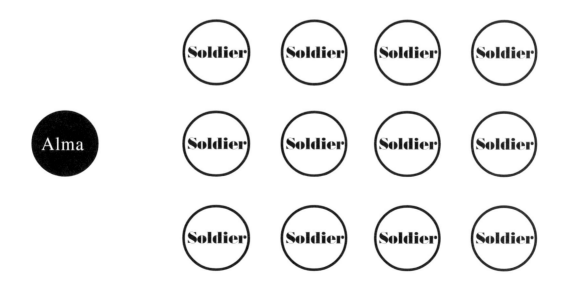

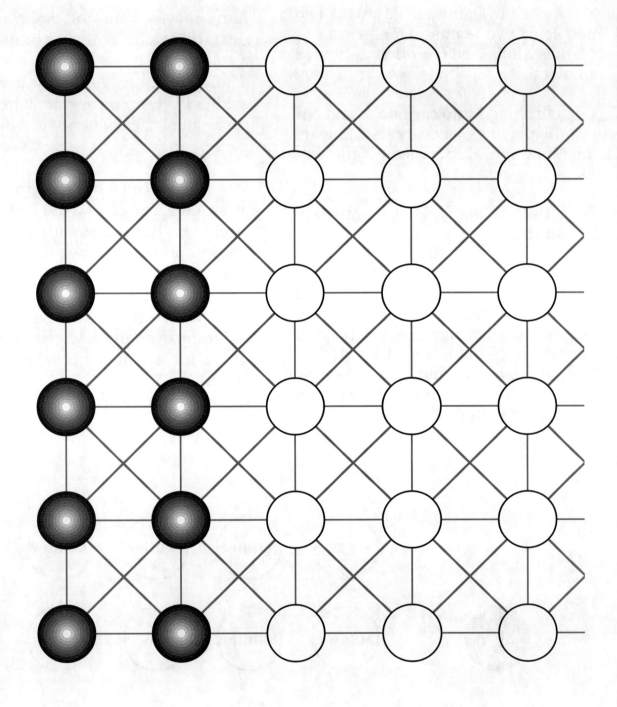

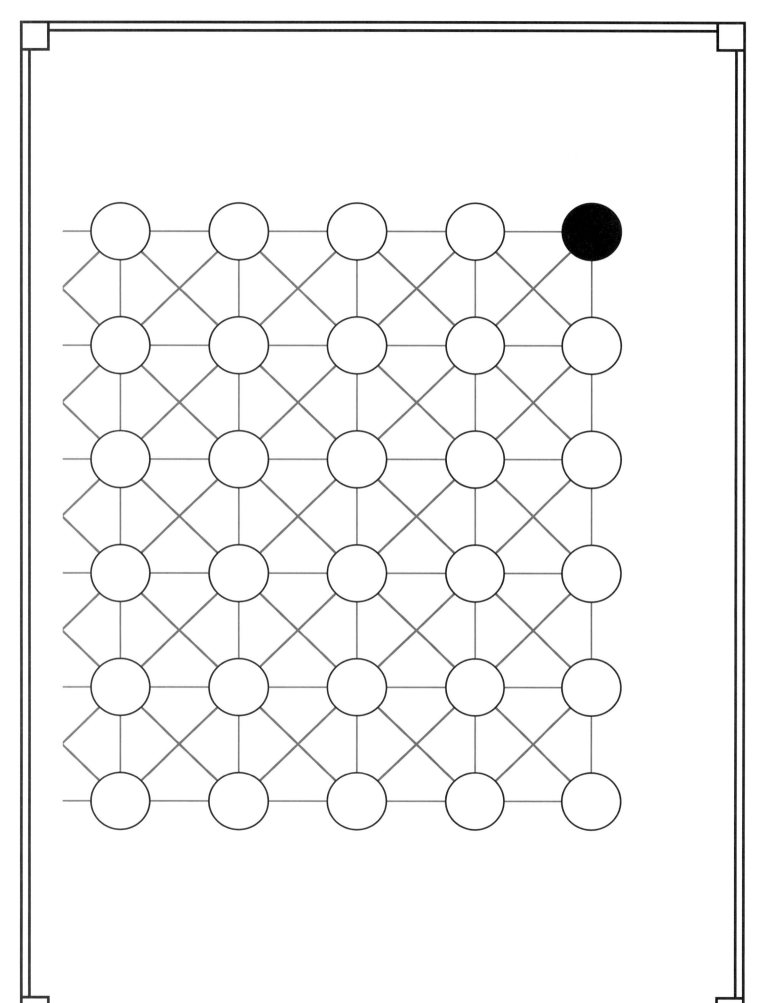

King Noah and the Lamanites

Mosiah 19

King Noah's army returned. They had not been able to catch Alma's people. The soldiers knew the king would not be happy.

They were right. King Noah was not happy. The people in Noah's kingdom were not happy, either. They thought King Noah was a bad king. They wanted someone else to be the king.

A man named Gideon lived in Noah's city in the land of Lehi-Nephi. Gideon did not like King Noah. He wanted to kill him and get a new king.

Gideon was big and strong. He drew his sword and attacked the king. King Noah tried to fight with Gideon, but Gideon was a better fighter.

King Noah ran away. Gideon chased him. The king turned to see how far away Gideon was. Gideon was just about to catch him!

King Noah ran to his tall, tall tower. He ran up to the very top. Gideon raced up the stairs after him. He came closer and closer to the king.

Gideon reached the top of the tower. King Noah turned to face him and saw something far away. The something was moving! The king looked harder. He saw that the something was an army. The Lamanite army was coming to attack his city!

The king shouted to Gideon, "Gideon, please don't kill me. The Lamanites

are attacking our city. I need to lead my people. If I don't, they will be destroyed by the Lamanites."

King Noah was more worried about himself than his people, but Gideon believed him. Gideon let the king go.

King Noah commanded his people to run away from the city. The Lamanite army ran after them. Then the Lamanites caught and began killing them.

King Noah told all of the men to leave their wives and children behind. He needed the strong men to survive. He didn't want the slower women and children to keep the men from running fast.

Some of the men would not leave their families. They said, "We would rather die with them than leave them behind."

The men who stayed behind had a plan. They told their daughters to stand at the front of their group of people. The daughters were very beautiful. They cried out to the Lamanites, "Please don't kill us. Please don't destroy our people."

The Lamanites liked the young women. The Lamanite soldiers listened to the girls and decided not to hurt them or their families.

The Lamanites took them back to the city. The Lamanite king told them, "You are our prisoners now. You may live in your houses and plant crops on the land. In return, you must give us half of everything you have now and half of anything you get in the future."

The poor people had to give the Lamanites half of all they had. Half of their gold, silver, and jewels. Half of their animals. Half of their hay, wheat, corn, and other crops. And half of anything they grew or made, year after year.

One of Noah's sons was among the prisoners. His name was Limhi. He was a good man. The people wanted him to be their king. Limhi agreed to lead them.

King Limhi was a very good king. The people were poor, but there was no fighting in the land. They paid their tax and lived in peace for many years.

Why did Gideon attack King Noah?

Why did Noah want Gideon to stop?

Why did the Lamanites spare the peoples' lives?

What kind of taxes did the prisoners have to pay?

Crossword

Use the words at the bottom of the page to fill in the blanks in this crossword puzzle. Have fun!

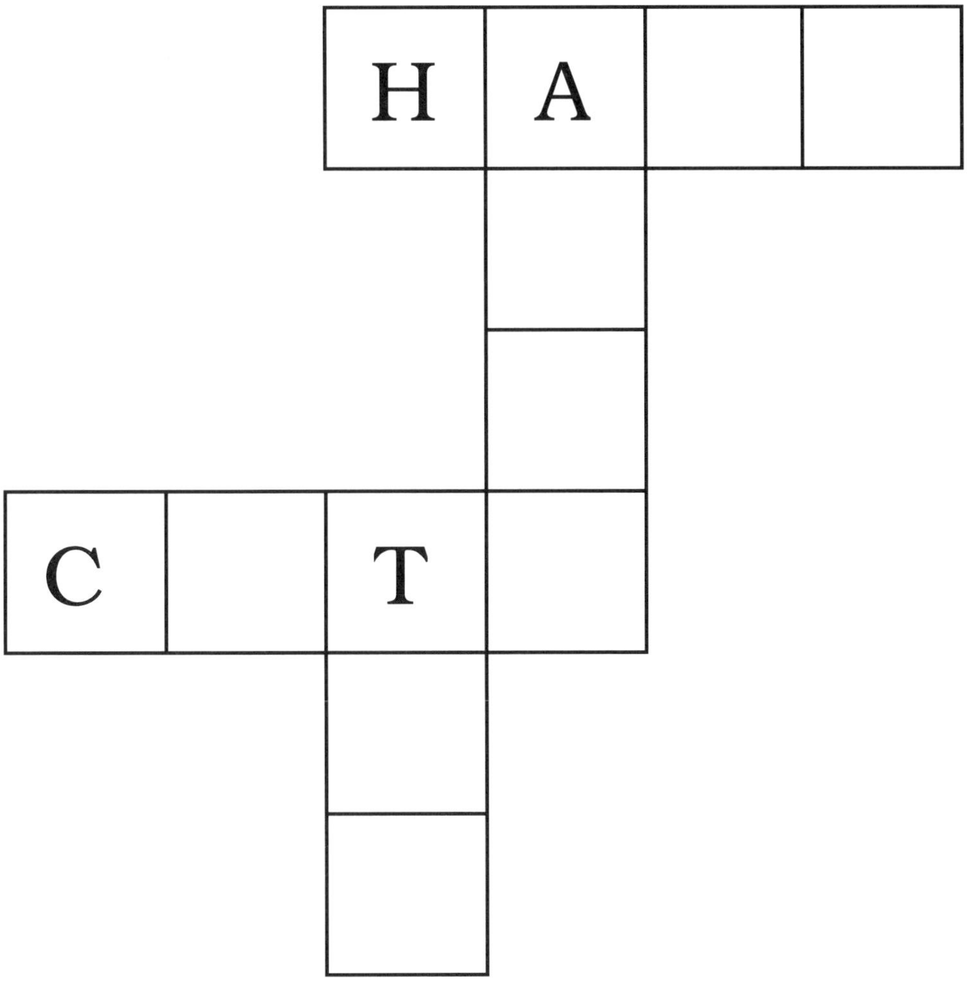

TAX

CITY

ARMY

HALF

Look It Up!

Look up Mosiah 19:7, 13, & 15 to fill in the blanks.

7 And now the king cried out in the anguish of his soul, saying: (3)_____, spare me, for the Lamanites are upon us, and they will (4)_____ us, yea, they will destroy my people.

13 And it came to pass that those who tarried with their (11)_____ and their (10)_____ caused that their fair (2)_____ should stand forth and (6)_____ with the Lamanites that they would not slay them.

15 Therefore the (7)_____ did spare their lives, and took them captives and carried them back to the land of Nephi, and granted unto them that they might possess the land, under the conditions that they would deliver up (14)_____ Noah into the hands of the Lamanites, and deliver up their (8)_____, even one half of all they (9)_____, one half of their (1)_____, and their (12)_____,

Crossword

Use the words you wrote on page 46 to fill in the blanks
in this crossword puzzle. Have fun!

and all their (5)_____ to the (13)_____ things, and thus they should pay king of the Lamanites from year to year.

King Benjamin

Mosiah 1

King Benjamin was ruler of Zarahemla, the city where the Nephites had lived for many years. Zarahemla was far away from the land of Lehi-Nephi. In fact, the people of Zarahemla were not sure if the people in Lehi-Nephi were still alive. They did not even know anything about King Noah, the Lamanites, or King Limhi.

King Benjamin was getting old, and he decided that it was time to pass the throne on to one of his sons.

He had three sons. Their names were Mosiah, Helorum, and Helaman. King Benjamin had taught them to read the scriptures and keep the commandments. They were good men.

King Benjamin asked Mosiah to gather all of the people together so that he could speak to them. Prince Mosiah travelled through the land asking the people to come and hear what the king had to say.

The people gathered around the temple. Each family set up a tent, with the door of each tent facing the temple. There were so many people that no one could count them all. Everyone wanted to hear their king.

King Benjamin had his servants build a high tower near the temple. From the tower, he could see his entire kingdom.

He climbed the tower and began to speak to his people. There were so many people that they could not all hear him. King Benjamin had scribes write what he said. Then the scribes carried the king's words throughout the crowd. The king wanted everyone to know what he said.

King Benjamin said to the people, "I have been a good king. I have treated you well." This was true. He had worked very hard to be fair and kind to his people. He had even worked to grow his own food so that he wouldn't be a burden to his people by living off of their taxes.

He said, "I have worked hard to serve you. I say this to teach you that when you serve each other, you are really serving Heavenly Father.

"I am old and will not live much longer. I am so weak now that I can hardly stand here to talk to you. I cannot be your king any more. My son, Mosiah, will be your king now."

Then King Benjamin taught the people about Jesus. He said, "Jesus Christ will come to earth some day. He will perform miracles. He will teach about Heavenly Father. He will die for our sins. Because of his death, we will be able to return and live with our Heavenly Father forever."

The king sent his scribes out to talk to the people. He wanted to see if the people believed what he had taught them. The scribes came back with good news: the people believed

and promised to serve the Lord. They never wanted to do bad things again. They only wanted to do good things for the rest of their lives.

King Benjamin was very happy. He told the people that from then on, they would be known as the children of Christ. They would be called this because they wanted to follow Christ's teachings. Their new name would always remind them that Jesus was their true ruler.

The people of Zarahemla lived happily and peacefully for many years. They always loved King Benjamin, and they loved their new king, King Mosiah.

What was King Benjamin's important message?

How can we serve Heavenly Father?

Look It Up!

Look up Mosiah 2:17. Use it to fill in the blanks below. Unscramble the letters from the squares. What is the secret message?

And __ __ __ __ __ __, I tell you these

__ __ __ __ __ __ that ye may learn

__ __ __ __ __ __; that ye may __ __ __ __ __ __

__ __ __ __ when ye are in the

__ __ __ __ __ __ __ of your

__ __ __ __ __ __ beings ye are only in the

__ __ __ __ __ __ __ of your __ __ __ .

Put the letters from the squares and circles here:

| P | | | | | | | | | | |

Now unscramble them here:

__ __ __ __ P __ __ __ __ __ __ __

50

King Mosiah

Mosiah 7-8, 21-22

King Mosiah had a small problem. His kingdom was peaceful. His people kept the commandments. Everyone should have been happy, but the people wanted something from their king. They wanted him to find out what had happened to their relatives who had gone to live in the land of Lehi-Nephi nearly eighty years before.

King Mosiah decided to send some of his men to find Lehi-Nephi. He chose a big, strong man named Ammon to lead the group. Ammon and fifteen other men set out the next morning.

They travelled for forty days in the wilderness. Finally, they found a big city. They set up their tents on a hill so that they could see into the city, but the people in the city could not see them.

Ammon took three men to the city. Their names were Amaleki, Helem, and Hem.

As they came near the city walls, they found a group of soldiers waiting for them. The soldiers tied them up and threw them in jail!

After two days, the king sent for Ammon and his friends. He told them, "I am King Limhi. Why did you come near us while I was walking outside the walls? Were you planning to hurt us?"

Ammon answered, "I am Ammon. I come from Zarahemla. My king sent us to find you."

King Limhi was very happy. He and his people still had to pay half of all their crops and earnings to the Lamanites. He said, "If you will help us escape from the Lamanites, we will be your slaves. We would rather serve you than the Lamanites."

King Limhi sent for the rest of Ammon's men. He gave them food and clothing. Ammon's men were very hungry from their journey.

King Limhi brought Ammon a book. He asked, "Can you read this? It is in a language that I cannot understand."

Ammon replied, "No. Our king, King Mosiah, could read it. He is a prophet. He can do anything the Lord wants him to do."

Limhi said, "It has been hard for us since the Lamanites took us prisoners. I sent some men to find Zarahemla.

"My men did not find Zarahemla, but they found a valley where a big battle had taken place. There were lots of weapons, armor and other things scattered all about. One of the things they found was this book, but it is in a strange language that we can't read. I would like to know what it says."

Ammon told King Limhi that he and his men would help Limhi's people escape. Then King Limhi could have King Mosiah read the strange book.

_____

Why was King Limhi happy to meet Ammon?

Why did he want to find Zarahemla?

Acronyms

An acronym is a group of letters that stand for each word in a phrase. For instance, the acronym "LDS" stands for "Latter-Day Saints." What acronyms can you create for the word "Alma"? How about "Faith"? Be creative! Our current favorite is: **A**lice **L**oathes **M**aking **A**pplesauce. What is yours?

A_____   L_____

M_____   A_____

F_____ A_____ I_____

T_____   H_____

A_____   L_____

M_____   A_____

F_____ A_____ I_____

T_____   H_____

A_____   L_____

M_____   A_____

Limhi's People Escape

Mosiah 22

King Limhi's people wanted to escape from the Lamanites. They wanted to live with the Nephites.

Ammon and King Limhi met with the people to make escape plans. Gideon, the man who fought King Noah, had a good plan. He wanted to pay the wine tax that the people owed. (They needed to give half of the wine that they made to the Lamanites.) Gideon wanted to pay all of the wine tax at once. They would give it to the Lamanite guards, who would drink it and become sleepy.

Everyone thought this was a good idea. The people gathered the jugs of wine. Then Gideon took the wine to the guards.

The guards were happy to take the wine tax. They wanted to drink it all up.

The guards drank and drank. They got very sleepy. Soon they fell into a deep sleep.

King Limhi and Ammon were ready. They had the people quietly gather all of the food and clothing that they could carry. They also gathered up all of their animals.

When they saw the sleeping guards, they knew that it was time to leave. They quietly tip-toed past the sleeping guards. The guards never woke up, even though many people and animals walked past them.

Ammon and King Limhi made the people walk as far as they could during that night. When they finally had to stop, they were very far away from their homes.

The Lamanite king was angry when he found out that his slaves had escaped. He sent soldiers after Limhi's people.

The soldiers tried to catch up, but Limhi's people were too far away. The soldiers finally had to stop. They returned to their king without any prisoners.

Ammon and his men led Limhi's people to Zarahemla. It took a long time to get there. They had to walk and walk.

When they finally reached Zarahemla, they were very happy. King Mosiah welcomed them into his city. Finally they were safe!

What was Gideon's plan?

Why were the people able to escape?

Why were the people happy to reach Zarahemla?

Maze

Help Gideon sneak past the sleeping guard.

Alma and Amulon

Mosiah 23-24

Do you remember Alma? He and his followers left Lehi-Nephi because they were afraid that King Noah would kill them for following Abinadi's teachings. They ran away from Noah's soldiers. They ran and ran, until they were far away from the city.

They found a safe place to live and built their own little city. They named it "Helam". They lived peacefully in Helam for several years. Alma was a kind ruler who used God's help to make wise decisions.

One day, something awful happened: the Lamanites found Helam! Alma's men saw the Lamanite army marching toward the peaceful little city.

Alma and his men met quickly to decide what to do. Should they try to fight the Lamanites? Or should they give up before their people got hurt? If they gave up, or if they lost the battle, they would become the Lamanites' slaves.

Alma reminded the people that the Lord had promised to keep them safe. The people were afraid, but they felt better when they heard Alma's words. They agreed that they should trust the Lord to protect them.

They decided not to fight. They gave up instead. They became the Lamanites' prisoners. The Lamanites made Amulon, a bad man, leader of the city of Helam.

This was the same Amulon who was one of King Noah's wicked priests. He still hated Alma, and he decided to be as mean as possible to him and the rest of the people who lived in Helam.

Amulon found creative ways to be mean. He made the people work hard. He punished them for anything he did not like. He made them speak his language. He did not believe in God, so he made it illegal to worship Heavenly Father. He even made it illegal to pray. He said that anyone who prayed would be put to death!

Alma and his people prayed anyway. In fact, they prayed as often as possible. They were very unhappy. They wanted to be free to worship as they chose.

Heavenly Father heard their prayers. He said, "Don't worry. I have heard your prayers. I will help you tomorrow."

Heavenly Father told Alma to get everyone ready to leave. During the night, Alma and the people gathered up all of their belongings. They gathered their animals. They gathered their crops. They got ready to escape.

Then the Lord made a miracle happen. In the morning, He caused the Lamanite guards to fall into a deep sleep. Alma, the people, and the animals walked right past the guards, and the sleepy soldiers never woke up!

When the people were far into the forest, they stopped to offer thanks to Heavenly Father for helping them. They knew that the Lord had done a miracle so that they could be safe.

Alma and his people walked and walked in the wilderness. Finally they came to the city of Zarahemla. King Mosiah joyfully welcomed them into his kingdom.

Zarahemla was full of people now. All of King Mosiah's people lived there. All of King Limhi's people lived there. And now all of Alma's people lived there. Things were getting kind of confusing. Who was in charge?

The three groups of people decided to become one large group. They called themselves "Nephites". King Mosiah was their king. Alma was the prophet and was the leader of the church. All of them were very happy.

Why did Amulon hate Alma?

What did Amulon do to make Alma's people unhappy?

What miracle did the Lord do?

How many kings lived in Zarahemla?

The people in Zarahemla had a king and a prophet. Do you think that having two rulers caused problems?

Reversals

Circle the answers to the questions below. This may be a little more difficult than it appears, because the answers are written backwards! Have fun!

Alma's people were running from whose army?

noedig   haon   ihmil   haisom

What was the name of Alma's city?

ihel   maleh   ihpen   almeharaz

What army found them?

etihpen   etimaroz   etinamal   etideraj

What did the people decide to do?

thgif   rednerrus   nur   hgual

Who did they trust to protect them?

rehtaf ylnevaeh   noluma   maleh

Who did the Lamanites make the leader of Helam?

amla   noedig   haon   noluma

King Limhi's Book

Omni, Mosiah 8, Ether 1-14, Genesis 11

Do you remember that King Limhi had a book he could not read? It was in a different language. It was made of sheets of brass. Limhi's men found it in the wilderness, in the ruins of an ancient city.

King Limhi brought the book to Zarahemla to see if King Mosiah could read it. King Mosiah agreed to do it. The book was the history of an ancient people, the Jaredites. They lived in the city of Babel, near Israel, a long time before Lehi lived there.

The people of Babel decided to build a large tower so that they could climb up to heaven. They used bricks to build the tallest tower anyone had ever seen. It reached up to the sky.

The Lord was not happy with the peoples' plan. He decided to change the peoples' language so that they could not talk to each other and make naughty plans. All of a sudden, each group of people spoke a different language! No one could understand anyone else. Everyone was confused and frightened.

Jared and his brother saw what was happening to the people of Babel. Jared said to his brother, "Pray to the Lord. Ask him not to change our language."

The brother of Jared prayed. The Lord heard his prayers and did not change the brothers' language. Also, the language of their friends and families was not changed.

The Lord told Jared's brother to gather together all of their animals, food, clothes, and other belongings. They would need to leave Babel.

Jared and his family and friends did as the Lord had said. They gathered all of the things they owned and went into the wilderness. The Lord led them to the edge of a great ocean.

The Lord told the brother of Jared to build eight small boats. He told him what materials to use and how the boats should be built. Jared's brother did exactly as he was told.

When the boats were finished, they had no windows. The brother of Jared prayed and said, "How will we see inside the boats? We cannot travel for a long time without light."

The Lord asked, "What do you want me to do?"

The brother of Jared thought for a while. Then he had an idea. He gathered sixteen clear, white stones.

Then he prayed. He said, "Oh Lord, I know that you can do anything. If you will just touch these stones with your finger, they will shine. Then we will be able to use them for light in our boats."

The Lord touched the stones with his finger. The brother of Jared saw the Lord's hand!

The Lord said, "You are able to see me because you have so much faith."

Then the Lord showed himself to the brother of Jared. The Lord had a body just like ours!

Jared and his friends and family got into the boats. The shining stones gave off plenty of light. The Lord made winds blow the boats all the way to the American continent.

The people of Jared, also called the Jaredites, built a great city and lived there for many years. They had children, and their children had children, until lots of people lived in the city.

The people divided into groups. The groups started to fight each other. Finally the Jaredites fought so much that all of their people were killed except one man. His name was Coriantumr. He lived alone in the abandoned city until King Limhi's time.

Many, many years later, King Limhi's men found the ruined city. They found the brass plates and the history of the Jaredites. King Mosiah translated the history, and we have it today.

Heavenly Father knew that He wouldn't change the Jaredites' language. Why did the brother of Jared have to pray for the Lord's help?

Why did Heavenly Father make Jared's brother solve the problem of the lights?

Why do we need to pray for help?

Look It Up!

Look up Ether 3:1, 6, 9 & 20 and fill in the missing words. Then use those words to fill in the blanks on the next page. What is the secret message?

1 And it came to pass that the brother of (2)_____, (now the number of the vessels which had been (1)_____ was eight) went forth unto the mount, which they called the mount Shelem, because of its exceeding height, and did molten out of a rock sixteen small (12)_____; and they were white and clear, even as transparent (14)_____; and he did (15)_____ them in his hands upon the top of the mount, and cried again unto the Lord. . .

6 And it came to pass that when the brother of Jared had said these words, behold, the (8)_____ stretched forth his (10)_____ and touched the stones one by one with his finger. And the veil was taken from off the (4)_____ of

the brother of Jared, and he saw the (6)_____ of the Lord; and it was as the finger of a (3)_____, like unto flesh and blood; and the brother of Jared fell down before the Lord, for he was struck with fear.

9 And the Lord said unto him: Because of thy (7)_____ thou hast seen that I shall take upon me (5)_____and blood; and never has man come before me with such exceeding faith as thou hast; for were it not so (11)_____ could not have seen my finger. . .

20 Wherefore, having this (13)_____
(9)_____ of God, he could not be kept from within the veil; therefore he saw Jesus; and he did (16)_____ unto him.

1. ___ ___ ___ ___ ___ ___ ___ ___ ___ ___ ___

2. ___ ___ ___ ___ ___ ___

3. ___ ___ ___ ___

4. ___ ___ ___ ___

5. ___ ___ ___ ___ ___

6. ___ ___ ___ ___ ___

7. ___ ___ ___ ___ ___

8. ___ ___ ___ ___

9. ___ ___ ___ ___ ___ ___ ___ ___

10. ___ ___ ___ ___ ___

11. ___ ___

12. ___ ___ ___ ___ ___ ___

13. ___ ___ ___ ___ ___ ___ ___

14. ___ ___ ___ ___ ___

15. ___ ___ ___ ___

16. ___ ___ ___ ___ ___ ___

Alma Learns a Lesson

Mosiah 27

Mosiah was a wise king. He and the prophet, Alma, led the people together. For a while everything was peaceful. But some of the members of the Church fell away. Soon there was a large group of people who actively worked against the Church.

Alma's son was one of these people. He was named Alma, after his father. We call him "Alma the Younger". (In this book, we will write his name like this: Alma. His father's name will look like this: Alma. That way, it will be easier for you to tell them apart.)

Alma and the sons of Mosiah tried to get people to leave the Church. One day, they were out walking in the countryside. An angel appeared to them in a cloud. The angel spoke in a voice as loud as thunder, saying, "Why are you trying to hurt the Church of God?"

Alma and the sons of Mosiah fell to the ground. They were so surprised, they could hardly understand what the angel was saying.

The angel spoke again: "Your fathers and the people of this city have been praying for Heavenly Father to make you stop doing bad things. Heavenly Father sent me here to tell you to be good."

Alma was so surprised and so scared that he could not speak. He was so weak that he could not move. His friends carried him to his father.

If your friends carried you home as weak as Alma was, how would your parents react? Wouldn't they be scared and worried? Alma was happy! He knew that only the power of God could have done this to his son.

Alma gathered all of the people together. He wanted them to see what had happened.

Everyone fasted for two days and two nights. They wanted Heavenly Father to help them and help Alma the Younger.

After two days, Alma got his strength back. He stood and began to teach. He said, "I have been born again. First I was physically born, like all of us were born. Then I was spiritually born. I am now a new person. I have repented of my sins. Heavenly Father forgave me."

Alma went throughout the land, telling everyone about his experiences. He became a great missionary.

Why did God send the angel to Alma?

Why wasn't Alma the Elder worried about his son?

How did this experience help to make Alma a good missionary?

Make-A-Word

See how many words you can make from the letters
in this phrase:

Alma the Younger

_____   _____   _____

_____   _____   _____

_____   _____   _____

_____   _____   _____

_____   _____   _____

_____   _____   _____

_____   _____   _____

_____   _____   _____

_____   _____   _____

The Sons of Mosiah

Mosiah 27-29

Alma's adventure with the angel changed his life. It also changed the lives of the people who were with him at the time. Four of these people were the sons of King Mosiah. Their names were Ammon, Aaron, Omner, and Himni.

These four brothers saw what happened to Alma. They saw him get his strength back. They saw how much he changed. They believed what Alma and the angel said. They decided to repent.

Ammon, Aaron, Omner, and Himni travelled throughout the land, trying to get people to believe in Christ. This was hard, because they had always taught people to leave the Church. Now they worked hard to repair some of the damage they had caused in the past.

Each became a great tool for Heavenly Father. He used them and their words to teach the people who needed to hear about the Gospel.

One day, the four brothers came to see their father, King Mosiah. They had a favor to ask him. They wanted to go teach the Lamanites about the Gospel.

King Mosiah didn't know what to say. He prayed for help to know what to do. It would be very dangerous for his sons to live among the Lamanites. The Lamanites killed any Nephites they found, and Mosiah was afraid for his sons' safety.

The Lord answered Mosiah's prayer. He told the worried father, "Let them go. They will bring many people to the Gospel. I will keep them safe."

King Mosiah had faith. He knew that Heavenly Father always keeps His promises. He let his sons go to the land of the Lamanites.

Now the king had another problem. He was getting old, and all of his sons were leaving to teach the Lamanites. He had no one to be the next king if he died.

Mosiah sent messengers throughout the land. They asked the people who should be the next king.

The messengers came back with news: The people wanted Aaron to be the next king.

Mosiah sent the men back to remind the people that Aaron and his brothers were gone and could not be king. Mosiah had an idea. He wrote a letter and sent it with the messengers. They read the letter to the people.

The letter said that King Mosiah agreed to be king for the rest of his life. He wanted the people to elect judges, though, to take over the job of running the kingdom.

Wise judges would make sure that the law was fair. If a judge wasn't fair, the people could elect some one else. This would be better than a king. The people had no way to get rid of a bad king.

The people thought this was a great idea. The people held elections and selected judges to take over the kingdom. Alma the Younger was elected Chief Judge. He made sure that all of the other judges were good.

He was also the prophet. He used the power of God to make good decisions for the kingdom.

Now the kingdom was secure. King Mosiah missed his sons, but he knew that they would be safe. He also knew that his people would be safe and happy.

Why couldn't one of Mosiah's sons become king?

Why did the Nephites decide to have an elected leader instead of a king?

Mix-up

These names are all mixed up. Can you unscramble them?

mlaa   ___ ___ ___ ___

hsimoa   ___ ___ ___ ___ ___ ___

nomam   ___ ___ ___ ___ ___

inihm   ___ ___ ___ ___ ___

ranoa   ___ ___ ___ ___ ___

rnmeo   ___ ___ ___ ___ ___

nijmaneb   ___ ___ ___ ___ ___ ___ ___ ___

ihlmi   ___ ___ ___ ___ ___

lzraehama   ___ ___ ___ ___ ___ ___ ___ ___ ___

mlaeh   ___ ___ ___ ___ ___

ihleihpne   ___ ___ ___ ___ - ___ ___ ___ ___ ___

The Chief Judge

Alma 1-4

Alma was a good ruler. He made good decisions. He prayed often, and the Lord told him what to do. Zarahemla was a nice place to live.

Even the nicest cities have bad people, however. A man named Nehor lived in Zarahemla. Nehor was lazy. He didn't like to work. He wanted to have other people pay him for preaching. Nehor felt that the people should pay for all of the Church leaders, instead of having them earn their own living.

Gideon was still living in Zarahemla. He was getting old, but he still fought for what he knew was right. He knew that Nehor was going to cause lots of trouble for the Church.

Gideon argued with Nehor. Nehor argued back. Pretty soon they were fighting. Gideon was old and not very strong, so he was killed in the fight.

The people brought Nehor to Alma. Alma was very unhappy. His friend Gideon was dead, and Nehor's words had caused arguments all through the city.

Alma said, "Nehor, you have done a very bad thing. You have caused my people to argue with each other, and you have killed a good man. Gideon followed the commandments and always chose the right. He did not deserve to die."

The law said that anyone who killed someone would have to be killed in return. Alma's soldiers took Nehor to the top of a hill. Nehor confessed that he had lied to the people and taught them bad things. Then the soldiers put him to death.

That did not end Alma's problems. In fact, things got worse and worse. The members of the Church were strong and followed the commandments. The people who fought against the Church grew stronger and louder and caused more and more problems. The two groups of people fought and argued all the time.

Finally, Alma decided that he needed more help. He stepped down as chief judge. From then on, he was the leader of the Church but not the leader of the city. The people elected a man named Nephihah to be their new chief judge.

Why was Gideon angry?

What lies did Nehor tell? Why would he lie?

What Do You Think?

What do think your house would have looked like
if you had lived in Zarahemla?   Draw your
house in the square below.

Word Links

Move from square to square to build words. Pick a square to begin your word, then move to any square which touches it (including diagonal ones). How many of the names from page 71 can you make?

A	M	N	E	R
A	M	O	I	H
U	R	N	M	B
O	L	J	E	I
N	M	A	M	N

Alma Goes on a Mission

Alma 5-8

Alma was happy. He didn't have to spend all of his time deciding the law any more! Since he wasn't the chief judge, he had time to do the thing he loved most of all: missionary work.

Alma started teaching anyone who would listen to him. First he taught people in Zarahemla. Then he started teaching in the cities outside of Zarahemla.

One day, he came to the city of Ammonihah. He began to teach there, just as he had taught in all of the other cities nearby.

The people in Ammonihah didn't want to hear his message. They attacked him and threw him out of the city.

Poor Alma was upset. He decided to go on to the next city. Maybe the people who lived there would be nicer than the ones in Ammonihah.

While he was walking to the next city, an angel came to him. The angel said, "You are a good man, Alma. You have been a good missionary, too. The Lord is happy with you. He wants you to go back to Ammonihah and try again."

What could Alma do? The Lord had told him to go back, so he turned around and ran as fast as he could back to Ammonihah.

When he got to the city, he was very hungry. He saw a man and asked him, "Could you please give a humble servant of God something to eat?"

The man took Alma to his house and fed him. The man's name was Amulek. Amulek was a wonderful person. He and Alma soon became friends.

The Lord told Alma, "Ask Amulek to come with you on your mission. Warn the people that if they do not repent, they will be punished." Amulek agreed to go with Alma.

Alma and Amulek became strong in the spirit. The Lord was with them always. He protected them wherever they went. Bad people tried to lock them in prison and tried to kill them. But the Lord took care of them and they were not hurt.

_____

Why did the Lord ask Alma to return to Ammonihah?

What kind of person was Amulek?

Look It Up!

Look up Alma 8:18 - 21 and fill in the blanks below. Then find those words in the word search on the next page.

18 Now it came to pass that after _____ had received his _____ from the angel of the Lord he returned _____ to the land of Ammonihah. And he entered the city by another way, yea, by the way which is on the south of the _____ of Ammonihah.

19 And as he entered the city he was an _____, and he said to a man: Will ye give to an _____ servant of God something to _____?

20 And the man said unto him: I am a _____, and

I know that thou art a holy _____ of God, for thou art the man whom an _____ said in a _____: Thou shalt _____. Therefore, go with me into my house and I will impart unto thee of my food; and I know that _____ wilt be a blessing unto me and my _____.

21 And it came to pass that the man received him into his house; and the man was called _____; and he brought forth bread and meat and set before Alma.

Word Search

```
A S N D T H E Y H A D P O W E R G
I P V E N U N L T O T H E M I N S
M E S S A G E R E C E I V E O M U
C E H T H G A T T H E Y I C O U L
D D N O N T B E C O N N S F I N E
D I I A N D U N G E E O I N S N E
I L T H H E R M W A P R O P H E T
S Y H U N G E R E D H I N T O P O
S S I M B L E T H A I A T A U N Y
M A N B R E A D C O T U L D S S L
A Y T L H E M N E V E E R T E H E
L E S E R V A N T S A M U L E K S
T H T E Y D I D C N O T E X E R C
I S H E T E A T H I E I R P O W E
R U O N T I L T H E T Y W E R E B
O U U N D I N B A N D Y S A N D C
A S T I N A L M A T O P R I S O N
```

When you have found all of the hidden words, read the letters which are left. They will form a hidden message. If you need help with the message, look up Alma 8:31.

Elder Amulek

Alma 11-12

One day while Alma and Amulek were teaching, a man came to them. The man's name was Zeezrom. He asked Amulek, "Could you answer a few questions for me?" Missionaries love to answer questions, so Amulek eagerly agreed.

But Zeezrom was not a good person. He liked to trick people with his words. He was trying to make Amulek do something bad.

Amulek must have been a little suspicious, because he told Zeezrom, "I will say only the things which the Spirit of the Lord tells me to say."

Zeezrom showed Amulek six large silver coins. Each coin was worth a lot of money. Six of these coins was enough money to feed two hungry missionaries for a very long time. Zeezrom asked Amulek, "If I give you these coins, will you say that there is no God?"

Amulek immediately said, "Why are you trying to tempt me? Do you believe there is no God? No, you do believe in God, but you love money more than you love Him."

Zeezrom asked, "How do you know there is a God?"

Amulek answered, "An angel told me."

Then Zeezrom knew that these men really were messengers from God. He began to shake with the knowledge that he had done many bad things.

Alma knew what Zeezrom was thinking. Alma told him, "God knows all your thoughts. He knows that you know the truth. He has seen you lie

to people again and again. You know that God is real."

Alma said, "The Devil is trying to use you to destroy good people. He will destroy you, too, if you don't repent."

Zeezrom began to shake even more than before. He was sure that Alma and Amulek could read his mind. He knew he was guilty of terrible things.

Zeezrom began to ask Alma and Amulek questions about God. He wasn't trying to trick them this time. He really wanted to know what they knew. Since Alma and Amulek were good missionaries, they answered all of his questions. They talked to him for a long, long time.

Alma taught him all about God and the Plan of Salvation. He taught Zeezrom what happened when he lied. He talked and talked and talked until all of Zeezrom's questions were answered.

Zeezrom believed what he heard. He decided to repent of his sins and become a better person.

_____

Why did Zeezrom shake and tremble?

How could Amulek know what Zeezrom was thinking?

Was it easy for Zeezrom to repent?

Can you be forgiven if you are bad?

Look It Up!

Look up Alma 11:26-31 and fill in the missing words. Then use the missing words to complete the puzzle on the next page.

26 And _____ said unto him: Thou sayest there is a _____ and _____ God?

27 And _____ said: Yea, there is a true and living God.

28 Now Zeezrom said: Is there _____than _____God?

29 And he answered, _____.

30 Now Zeezrom said unto him again: How _____ thou these _____?

31 And he said: An _____ hath made them known unto me.

Criss-Cross

This kind of crossword puzzle doesn't need numbers! Use the words from page 82 to fill in the blanks. Begin with the words which intersect with "Amulek", then gradually move outward. Have fun!

Prisoners!

Alma 12-14

While Alma and Amulek were teaching Zeezrom, people began to gather. They were curious and wanted to know what the two strangers were saying. Some of the people agreed with Alma. Others got angry at his words.

The people who believed Alma repented of their sins. They wanted to know more about Heavenly Father.

The people who didn't believe Alma got more and more angry. There were a lot more of these people, and they turned into an angry mob. They didn't like Alma telling them to repent.

The angry people tied up Alma and Amulek. They took the two missionaries to the chief judge of their city. They told the judge that Alma and Amulek were lying to the people and causing trouble in the city. The judge had them thrown into prison.

Poor Zeezrom! He had started all of this, but he knew the truth now. He tried to talk to the people and undo some of the wrong things he had taught, but the people wouldn't listen to him.

Alma and Amulek spent many days in the dark, filthy prison. The guards tied them up with thick ropes until they couldn't move. The guards didn't give them anything to eat or drink. They even took the missionaries' clothes away, so that they would be cold and miserable.

After many days, the chief judge came and stood before them. He said, "If you have the power of God, set yourselves free. Then we will believe you."

Many people had come with the chief judge, and each person said the same thing to Alma and Amulek. When the last person had teased them, the two men felt the power of the Lord come into them.

Alma and Amulek stood up and prayed out loud for strength. Then they broke the ropes which bound them. The people started to run, because they knew that God was angry with them. But they were so scared that they fell down and couldn't make it to the door.

The ground began to shake. The prison walls started to crack. Then the entire building fell apart. The heavy stones from the walls and ceiling fell on the chief judge and his friends and killed them.

Alma and Amulek were not hurt! They were the only people left alive in the ruined building. They calmly walked out of the pile of fallen stones.

The people who lived near the prison heard the noise and came running. When they saw that Alma and Amulek were alive and free, they were afraid. They turned around and ran away.

Alma and Amulek left Ammonihah. They wanted to teach people who would listen to their message.

Why weren't Alma and Amulek hurt by the fire or the falling stones?

Does the Lord protect all missionaries with fire?

Did Alma and Amulek still want to be missionaries after they were treated so badly?

Maze

Help Alma and Amulek find their way out of the ruined prison.

Freedom!

Zeezrom Repents

Alma 15

Alma and Amulek left Ammonihah, where the people were so mean to them. They went to the city of Sidon, where Zeezrom lived.

Zeezrom was very ill. He felt sad and guilty because his words and actions had caused the deaths of Alma and Amulek. He didn't know that the two missionaries were safe. He only knew what he had seen. He became so sick that he got a very high fever. He thought he was going to die.

When he found out that Alma and Amulek were in Sidon, he asked for them to come to him. They came, and Alma gave him a blessing. He said, "Oh Lord, bless this man that he may be healed if his faith is strong enough."

Zeezrom's faith was strong enough. As soon as Alma said those words, Zeezrom jumped to his feet and began to walk around. He was healed!

Alma baptized Zeezrom. Zeezrom began to go about the city, teaching anyone who would listen to his message.

_____

Why was Zeezrom so sick?

Did Zeezrom have enough faith?

What does this story teach us about faith?

Acrostic Poem

An acrostic poem is one in which the first letter of each line forms a word. Here is an example:

Try it!

Amulek
Missionary of God
Under His power
Loved the people
Eagerly taught believers
Knew the true love of God

A_____

M_____

U_____

L_____

E_____

K_____

Alma Meets Some Old Friends

Alma 17

Alma and Amulek left Sidon after they baptized Zeezrom. They wanted to teach the people in the land of Manti. While they were walking, they saw some men in the distance. As the men came closer, Alma recognized them. The men were Ammon, Aaron, Omner, and Himni, the sons of Mosiah.

Alma and his friends were so glad to see each other that they could hardly contain their joy. They had had many wonderful experiences together and were close friends. Mosiah's sons were there when the angel appeared to Alma. They carried him to his father and waited until he was healed. They had preached together in Zarahemla.

The five friends had not seen each other since Ammon and his brothers left Zarahemla to become missionaries. Fourteen years had passed, and Alma was eager to hear about his friends' adventures.

As the men talked, Alma became even more joyful. He was happy to see them, but he was even more happy when he learned that they still had strong testimonies of the Gospel. His friends had tried their best to serve the Lord all of these years, and Alma rejoiced at that news.

How long had it been since the friends had last seen each other?

What made Alma even more happy?

Scrambled Picture

Copy this page onto cardstock and cut the pieces apart on the dotted lines. Can you put the picture back together? Who are these four men?

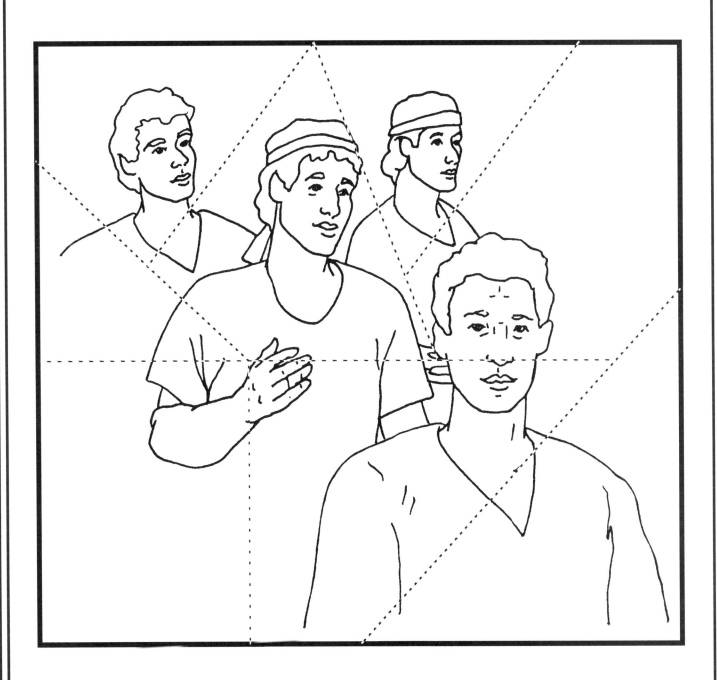

The Lord's Tools

Alma 17

When Ammon and his brothers left Zarahemla, they went into the wilderness. They took their swords, spears, bows, arrows, and slings with them so that they could catch food during their journey. They also brought several of their friends who also wanted to be missionaries.

The small group of men walked for many days in the wilderness. They fasted and prayed for the Lord's help. They wanted to go where the Lord needed them. They needed Him to tell them where to go.

They also needed to have Heavenly Father's spirit with them so that they could be good teachers. They wanted to be good tools for the Lord to use.

The spirit of the Lord came to them. It said, "Be comforted." They felt better. The Lord also told them that they would be used to teach many of the Lamanite people who needed to hear the Gospel.

When the brothers reached the border of the Lamanites' land, they separated. Each went to a different Lamanite city. That way, the four brothers and their friends would be able to teach people in four cities at the same time.

The four brothers were a little nervous about teaching the Lamanites. They had a good reason to be nervous: the Lamanites were a wild, ferocious people.

Lamanites killed Nephites as often as possible. They wanted precious things like silver and jewels, but they didn't want to work for them. Instead, they killed and robbed anyone who had what they wanted.

The brothers had faith. They had been told by the Lord that they would be safe. It took a lot of courage to go into the Lamanite cities, but Ammon and his brothers remembered the Lord's promises and did as they were commanded.

_____

What does this story teach us about faith?

Why did the four brothers decide to go on a mission to the Lamanites?

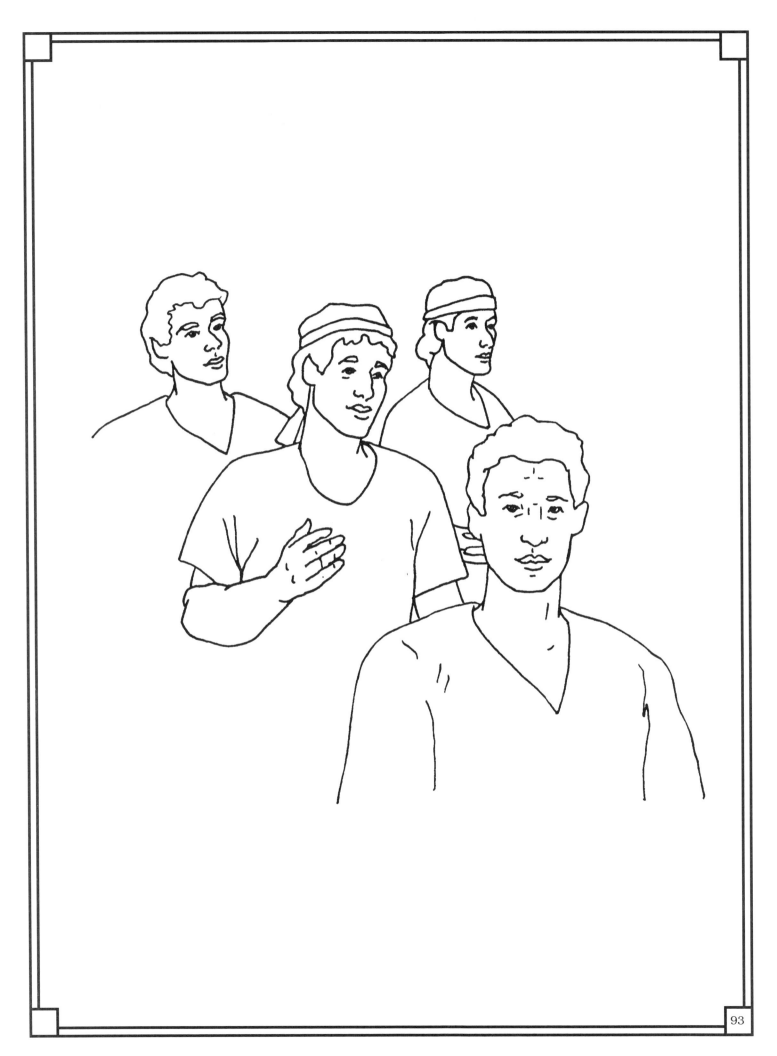

The Lord's Toolbox

Heavenly Father has some unusual tools. Unscramble the
names below to find out who the Lord used as
His tools in Book of Mormon times.

LMAA   __ __ __ __

LMUAKE   __ __ __ __ __ __

MNOAM   __ __ __ __ __

NORAA   __ __ __ __ __

MRNOE   __ __ __ __ __

IMHNI   __ __ __ __ __

HNEIP   __ __ __ __ __

HELI   __ __ __ __

BCOAJ   __ __ __ __ __

SIAMHO   __ __ __ __ __ __ __

NESO   __ __ __ __

Word Search

Can you find the hidden words? When you
have found them, draw a circle around them.

```
A  L  M  A  S  D  G  J
W  S  D  E  H  P  L  K
E  R  T  O  O  L  S  Q
A  A  R  O  N  I  L  N
P  O  I  U  Y  U  H  B
R  F  A  I  T  H  W  E
```

ALMA   AARON

TOOLS   FAITH

Ammon's Adventures

Alma 17

Ammon went to the Land of Ishmael. As soon as he crossed into the Lamanites' city, they arrested him. They took him to the king. The law stated that the king could do anything he wanted to do to prisoners.

The king's name was Lamoni. He was not happy to find a Nephite in his kingdom. He asked if Ammon intended to live in his city.

Ammon answered, "Yes, I do. I want to live here for a long time. I might even stay here until I die."

King Lamoni was so pleased with the young man's manner that he had Ammon untied. He even offered to let Ammon marry one of his daughters! (Now *there* was a persuasive missionary!)

But Ammon said, "No, thank you. I would rather be your servant." So Ammon became the king's servant. He was sent with a group of people to watch over the king's flocks.

The flocks of sheep needed to have water, so Ammon and the other servants took them to the local watering place. As they came near, some of the other shepherds ran and scattered the king's sheep.

It was the custom of some of the Lamanites to work together to steal other peoples' sheep. Some of the robbers would scatter the sheep, and the rest of the robbers would run in and take as many as they could. This is what happened this day.

The sheep ran in all directions, and the servants were afraid. They knew that if they returned without the sheep, the king would have them killed. They began to cry.

When Ammon saw what was happening, his heart was filled with joy. Here was a perfect opportunity to teach these people about the power of the Lord!

He got the servants to stop crying and gather up the sheep. Once that was done, the bad men came again to scatter the flocks.

Ammon told the servants to form a circle around the sheep to protect them. He would take care of everything else.

The bad men were not afraid of Ammon. After all, there was only one Ammon, and there were lots of them.

They did not know that they should be very afraid, indeed. The Lord had promised to protect Ammon and his brothers, and Ammon intended to test that promise. He began throwing rocks at the robbers.

Ammon threw the rocks so hard that he killed a few of the men. The rest of the bandits were surprised and angry and rushed to attack him. They had big clubs and raised them to hit Ammon.

Then a miracle happened! Every man who lifted his club to hit Ammon suddenly felt the sting of Ammon's sword. Ammon cut off the arms of his attackers. He cut off the arm of anyone who raised a sword against him.

After he had cut off many of the men's arms, the bandits became afraid. They turned and ran away. He ran after them.

He chased them far away, then returned to help the other servants. They gathered up all of the arms lying on the ground. They went to show the arms to the king and tell him what had happened.

Do you think that Ammon was scared of Lamoni? Why?

Why didn't Ammon marry the princess?

Why was he glad when the robbers attacked?

Elimination

What did Ammon say to King Lamoni? Cross out words in the boxes below until only the message is left.

1. Cross out all words that have the letter "P".

2. Cross out all words which end with "R".

3. Cross out all words which contain "M".

4. Cross out all words that end in "S".

5. Cross out all words which contain "C".

6. Cross out all words that end with "D".

7. Cross out all words which have "K" in them.

Crying	King	Sheep	Protect
Rocks	I	Circle	Lamoni
Ammon	Miracle	Will	Robbers
Clubs	Marry	Daughter	Attack
Be	Kill	Arms	Sword
Bandits	Thy	Afraid	Servant

The Conversion of Lamoni

Alma 18-19

Ammon and the other servants returned to the castle. Ammon went to feed and harness King Lamoni's horses. The king had told them to get his chariot ready when they returned from watering the sheep.

The other servants went to King Lamoni and told him what had happened. When he saw all of the arms, he had to believe their incredible story. When he learned about Ammon's loyalty and faithfulness, he was astonished. He said, "Ammon is no ordinary man. He must be the Great Spirit himself!"

All of the servants were afraid. They had grown up hearing the stories of the Great Spirit, the god who would come and visit the Lamanites. They were afraid that the Great Spirit would not be happy with the way they had lived their lives.

Lamoni was afraid, too. He was the leader of a fierce, bloodthirsty people. He had committed many murders. He had had many servants killed when their flocks were scattered. This was legal according to the Lamanites' laws, but Lamoni was afraid that the Great Spirit might not approve anyway.

Lamoni asked, "Where is Ammon?" The servants told him that Ammon was feeding and harnessing the horses for the king's journey.

Lamoni was astonished. Ammon remembered such a minor command, even after fighting a battle. What a faithful servant!

After Ammon finished with the horses, he went to see the king. He asked, "What would you like me to do now?"

Lamoni didn't answer him for an entire hour. Since loyal, polite servants would never speak before the king answered the question, Ammon waited patiently. Finally he asked again, "What would you like me to do?"

King Lamoni still didn't answer. But the Spirit told Ammon what the king was thinking. Ammon asked, "Are you wondering how I saved your flocks? Why are you afraid of me? I am just a man, and I am your loyal servant. I will always work hard for you."

The king was even more amazed as he realized that Ammon could read his mind. Finally Lamoni asked, "Who are you? What are you? Are

you the Great Spirit, who knows all things?"

Ammon answered and said, "No, I am not."

The king demanded, "How do you know what I am thinking? Tell me how you do these things. Tell me how you were able to kill so many robbers. Tell me how you had the strength to cut off so many arms. If you will tell me these things, I will give you anything you want."

Ammon was kind and good. He knew that he could make the king give him any valuable thing in the kingdom or do anything he wanted. But instead of asking for riches, he merely said, "What I want is for you to listen to what I have to say." What a great missionary!

Ammon then taught King Lamoni about Heavenly Father. He taught the king that what he knew as the Great Spirit was really God, our Father. He told Lamoni about Jesus and how we can all be saved from our sins because of His atonement.

King Lamoni said, "I believe all that you have taught me. Are you sent from God?"

Ammon answered, "I am just a man. I was born just like any other man.

But I have been called of God to teach your people. You need to know about the Gospel so that you can repent and live with Heavenly Father forever. As long as I am faithful, the Lord will tell me what to teach you so that you can be happy."

King Lamoni believed Ammon's words. He began to pray out loud. He begged, "Oh Lord, please have mercy on me and my people."

When he had said this, he fell to the ground. He looked like he was dead. His servants carried him to the queen, who thought he was dead. She began to cry, and so did her children. They thought their father had died.

Lamoni lay on his bed for two days and nights. The queen made plans for his funeral. She was very unhappy. She thought her husband was dead. But somehow, she just couldn't give up on him.

Was Ammon proud of what he did?

When should you take credit for what you do, and when should you give the Lord credit for what happened?

Was King Lamoni really dead?

Word Circles

The letters in these circles spell words--but you have to decided where the words begin! And remember: the words can be spelled either clockwise or counter-clockwise. Write the words on the lines below the circles.

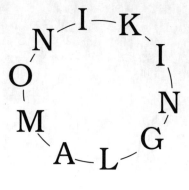

_____

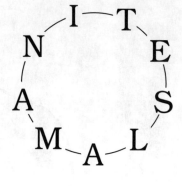

_____

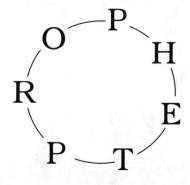

_____

Acrostic Poem

Did you like doing the poem from page 89? Here's another kind of acrostic--each line only has one word. Here's an example:

Alma,
Loving
Missionary
Always

A_____

M_____

M_____

O_____

N_____

L_____

A_____

M_____

O_____

N_____

I_____

A Faithful Queen

Alma 19

The queen had an idea. She had heard about Ammon and his great powers. Maybe Ammon could do something to help her.

She sent for Ammon. When he arrived, she told him, "My servants say that you are a prophet of a holy God and that you have power to do mighty things in His name. If this is true, I want you to go to my husband and heal him. Everyone thinks he is dead, but I don't know."

Now this was what Ammon wanted most of all. He knew that the king was overcome by the Spirit and was learning great things. The king was still alive, but the great things he was learning were so amazing and wonderful to him that he fainted and remained unconscious for two days and nights.

Ammon went to Lamoni. He told the queen, "He is not dead. He is asleep, and tomorrow he will wake up. Don't bury him yet. Do you believe what I am telling you?"

She answered, "I have no information except what you have told me. But I believe you anyway."

Ammon said to her, "You have a lot of faith. Such faith has never been seen among the Nephites. You are a special person."

The next day, the king awoke. He stood up and held out his hand to his wife and said, "Blessed be the name of God and blessed are you. I have been taught many great things."

Ammon was delighted. The Lord had used him as a tool to work a miracle among these people. That was Ammon's only desire.

What really happened to King Lamoni?

Why did the queen believe Ammon?

What does this story teach us about faith?

Look It Up!

Look up Alma 19:4-5, 9-10 and fill in the missing words.
Then use them to complete the puzzle on the next page.

4 And she said unto him: The _____ of my _____ have made it known unto me that thou art a _____ of a holy God, and that thou hast _____ to do many mighty works in his name;

5 Therefore, if this is the case, I would that ye should go in and see my husband, for he has been laid upon his bed for the space of two days and two _____; and some say that he is not dead, but others say that he is _____ and that he stinketh, and that he ought to be placed in the sepulchre; but as for myself, to me he doth not stink.

9 And Ammon said unto her: Believest thou this? And she said unto him: I have had no _____ save thy word, and the_____ of our servants; nevertheless I _____ that it shall be

Criss-Cross

Use the missing words from page 108 to fill in the Criss-Cross. Begin with the words which intersect with "Believe", then gradually move outward. Have fun!

B E L I E V E

according as thou hast said.

10 And Ammon said unto her: Blessed art thou because of thy exceeding _____;

I say unto thee, woman, there has not been such great faith among all the _____ of the Nephites.

Abish Knows What to Do

Alma 19

The queen had a servant who was no ordinary person. Her name was Abish. She already knew about the Gospel.

When she was a child, her father had a remarkable dream. In this dream, he learned about Heavenly Father and Jesus. All of Abish's life, she had heard about this special dream.

As she grew up, she prayed about what she had learned. The Lord taught her many things through the Spirit. She was not a great prophet, and she wasn't rich or powerful. She was just a regular person who believed in God.

God loved her and taught her great things. As a result, she had the blessings of the Gospel long before Ammon came to her city. She knew that God loves all of us equally and blesses us when we are faithful.

Abish was in the king's room when he woke up and began to speak. She heard him say, "Behold, I have seen my Redeemer, and he will be born and die. He will save us all from our sins."

Then she saw him fall down again, unconscious. The queen was also overcome by the Spirit and fainted. Abish saw Ammon fall to his knees and begin thanking Heavenly Father for all that had happened. Then Ammon was overcome by the Spirit and fainted also.

The king's servants were frightened and began to pray. They also fell to the ground, unconscious.

Abish was the only one in the room who remained conscious. She knew that something wonderful had happened. All of these people had been overcome by the Spirit. All of them were learning great things.

Abish wanted everyone to see what had happened and learn about Heavenly Father. She ran from house to house, telling the townspeople what had happened in the palace. A large group of people gathered. They were astonished when they saw all of the bodies lying on the ground in the king's bedroom.

The people saw their king, their queen, and the king's servants lying

on the ground as if they were dead. Then they saw Ammon. Ammon was a Nephite. Nephites were the enemy. Also, Ammon had killed several people while he was saving the king's flocks.

One of the men in the room had a relative who was killed by Ammon. This man was angry. He drew his sword and attacked Ammon. As he lifted his sword, he fell to the ground. He was dead.

When the rest of the people saw this, they were very afraid. They began to wonder if Ammon was the Great Spirit. Some thought he was, and some thought he wasn't. They began to argue. The argument went on and on.

Abish saw that instead of learning about God, these people were only fighting. She was so disappointed that she began to cry.

Abish went to the queen and clasped her hand. As soon as she touched the queen, the queen woke up. She stood up and began to teach the people the wonderful things she had learned.

The queen touched King Lamoni's hand. He woke up and began to speak. He told his people that they needed to repent of their sins.

He taught them about Jesus and Heavenly Father.

Many of the people in the room understood what the king was saying. They believed his words.

Some of the people didn't believe the king. They left the palace.

The believers stayed and learned and learned. Pretty soon they wanted to be baptized. Ammon baptized them.

The people became a righteous people. They didn't want to do bad things any more. Instead, they only wanted to do good things. They became good people who worked together and worshipped together.

This was the beginning of the Lord's work among the Lamanites. The Lord turned a fighting people into a loving, caring people. He will help anyone who will sincerely try to learn about Him.

_____

Why was Abish sad?

Why didn't the people want to do bad things any more?

How did they become a loving, caring people?

Can the same thing happen to us?

Look It Up!

Look up Alma 19:29 - 31 and fill in the missing words. Then find those words in the Word Search on the next page.

29 And it came to pass that she went and took the queen by the hand, that _____ she might raise her from the _____; and as soon as she _____her hand she arose and stood upon her feet, and _____with a loud voice, _____: O blessed Jesus, who has saved me from an awful hell! O blessed God, have _____on this people!

30 And when she had said this, she clasped her hands, being filled with joy, _____many words which were not understood; and when she had _____ this, she took the _____, _____, by the hand, and behold he arose and stood upon his _____.

31 And he, immediately, _____ the contention among his _____, went forth and began to _____ them, and to _____them the words which he had heard from the mouth of Ammon; and as many as heard his words believed, and were _____ unto the Lord.

Word Search

Find the words from page 114. When you have found all of them, the circles around them will form another word. What is this secret word?

```
M E R C Y J T E A C H S T J K S A S J L O I M
E I E C R I O T U R E S R E I S P R A P T O R
M N B R E F U Y U T K M K M N A R E F Y Y U T
H G U U O M C R I E D B A H H L A M O N I I A
E D K R Y T H H I T R C A R D W R Y T Y H N T
L O E S N D E V G S N O E L O B S N D P V G G
O M D E B E D O N E J P V O M X E B E R S A N
R O E T N J Z A T D K M H R M C U N K P A T D
U S E E I N G M H I I A S U Q O T N J Z M H I
M P P O U K A R E R N N Y M E N O U K A R E R
C E I B E S R M R I G D S C R V B E S R M R I
W A U P O U A Y I T P E O P L E P O U A Y I T
E K S A G E H U T N F E M E S R A G E H U T N
Y I T I R P E L A M E N D Y O T I R H E G A R
E N M E R R L K N V E T T E M E L E J M K N V
A G R O U N D H K L T S A T O D E R R L H K L
N I U Y T D A O P Y F T B N I U Y T D A O P Y
```

What is the secret word? _____

How many teachers can you find in this story? How can you be that type of teacher? Are you part of the Lord's toolbox?

Ammon Rescues His Brothers

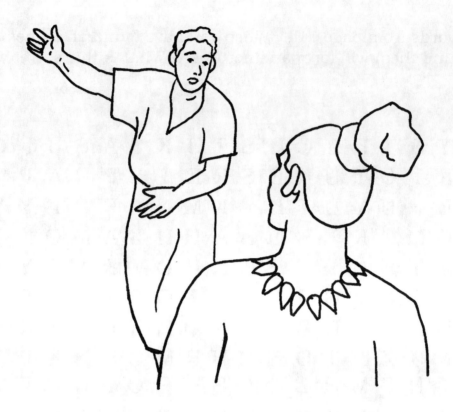

Alma 20

Lamoni was a king. There were many other kings who ruled small kingdoms near his. All of these kings were ruled by a more powerful king. This type of king is called a "High King", because he rules over many small kingdoms. The High King of the Lamanites was Lamoni's father.

The High King was planning a great feast. The feast would be held to honor the High King's sons and several of the other kings.

Lamoni was invited to the feast. He prepared to journey to the High King's castle. He invited Ammon to go with him.

The voice of the Lord came to Ammon and told him, "If you go with Lamoni, the High King will try to kill you. Instead, go to the land of Middoni. Your brothers and friends are in prison there."

Ammon told Lamoni that he had to go to Middoni and could not go with him to the High King's feast. Lamoni said, "The king in Middoni, King Antiomno, is my friend. I will go with you and help you free your brothers." This was very brave and loyal of Lamoni, because it could be quite dangerous to ignore a summons from the High King.

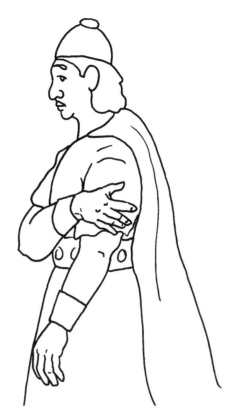

Lamoni asked, "Who told you that your brothers are in prison?"

Ammon told him that the Lord had spoken to him. When Lamoni heard this, he had his servants get his chariots ready immediately. He knew that if the Lord said to do something, he'd better obey quickly.

While Ammon and Lamoni were riding to Middoni, they met the High King. He was upset that Lamoni did not come to his feast. When he heard why, he was even more angry. He chastised Lamoni for listening to a Nephite. Then he ordered Lamoni to kill Ammon.

King Lamoni said, "I will not kill Ammon. I am going to Middoni to save his brothers and friends, because I know that they are good men. I know that they were sent here by God."

When the High King heard this, he was even more angry. He drew his sword and attacked Lamoni. Ammon tried to reason with the two kings. He said, "If you kill your son, you will kill an innocent man."

The High King said, "I know that. You are the guilty one. I should be killing you instead." And he lifted his sword to kill Ammon.

But Ammon was a good fighter, and he had the Lord on his side. He defended himself. He saw an opening and struck the King's sword arm. The king could not fight any more. He was afraid that Ammon would kill him.

He was desperate to save his own life and begged Ammon not to kill him. He said, "If you spare my life, I will give you anything you wish. You can even have half of my kingdom."

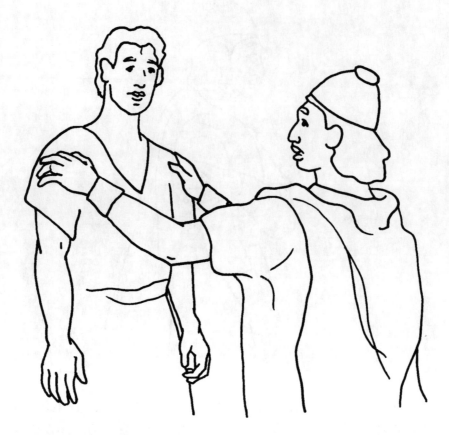

This was the second time that Ammon had been granted a wish. Again, he could be a very wealthy man if he wanted to. Instead, he told the king, "I want you to free my brothers and their friends. I also want you to let Lamoni keep his kingdom and worship as he chooses. If you will do these things, I will spare your life."

When the High King realized how loyal Ammon was to Lamoni, he was amazed. He granted Ammon's requests. He also asked Ammon to bring his brothers to his own castle to teach him. He wanted to learn more about what Lamoni had been learning.

Ammon and Lamoni resumed their journey to Middoni. When they got there, they were very sad to see Ammon's brothers. The poor men had been treated very badly. They had had no food or water, and their clothes had been taken away so that they would be cold. They had been beaten and tightly tied up with ropes which caused wounds where they touched the men's bodies.

The men knew that they were doing what the Lord wanted them to do, and they were patient and kind to their tormentors. However, they were very glad to see Ammon!

Ammon and Lamoni returned to Lamoni's castle. Ammon remained there for many years. He set up churches throughout the kingdom. He taught the people. The people tried to keep the commandments. It was a happy kingdom for many years.

Why didn't Ammon take half of the High King's kingdom?

Why would anyone throw a missionary in jail?

Mosiah's Family

Who were Mosiah's children? Put their names in the boxes below.

Ammon

Aaron

Himni

Omner

Look It Up!

Look up Alma 20:3-4 and fill in the missing words. Under each letter is a number. Place that letter in the corresponding blank on the next page.

3 Now it came to pass that when Ammon had heard this, he said unto Lamoni: Behold, my brother and brethren are in prison at Middoni, and I go that I may

___ ___ ___ ___ ___ ___ ___them.
26 23 12 20 18 15 27

4 Now___ ___ ___ ___ ___ ___
      12 17 14 3   4   20

said unto Ammon: I know, in the strength of the Lord thou canst do all things. But

___ ___ ___ ___ ___ ___, I will
22 5   6   25 12 13

go with thee to the land of

Middoni; for the king of the land of Middoni, whose ___ ___ ___ ___ is
                    4   7   14 23

___ ___ ___ ___ ___ ___ ___ ___,
17 4   21 20 2   14 1   11

is a friend unto me; therefore I go to the land of Middoni,

___ ___ ___ ___ I may flatter the
21 9   7   10

___ ___ ___ ___ of the land, and
28 20 1   24

he will cast thy brethren out of prison. Now Lamoni

___ ___ ___ ___ unto him: Who
16 17 20 26

told ___ ___ ___ ___ that thy
     8   9   19 15

brethren were in prison?

120

Fill In The Blanks

Using the missing words from page 120, find the letters which have the same numbers as the letters on this page. When you finish "decoding" the secret message, you will have Ammon's answer to Lamoni's question.

___ ___   ___ ___ ___
1   2   3   4   5

___ ___ ___ ___   ___ ___ ___ ___
6   7   8   9   10   11   12   13

___ ___   ___ ___ ___ ___
14   15   16   17   18   19

___ ___   ___ ___   ___ ___ ___
20   21   22   23   24   25   26

Teaching the King

Alma 22 - 23

After Aaron and his friends were saved by Ammon and Lamoni, they were told by the Lord to go to the castle of the High King.

The king was glad to see them. He had lots of questions for them. He had been thinking about what Ammon and Lamoni had told him.

Aaron asked, "Do you believe there is a God?"

The king answered, "If you say there is a God, then I will believe you." Then the king asked, "What is repentance and why is it important? Ammon told me I need to repent or be punished."

Aaron answered him and taught him about Heavenly Father, Jesus, and the Plan of Salvation. He taught the king that because Jesus would die for all peoples' sins, anyone could repent and be forgiven.

The High King listened to Aaron's words. He believed what Aaron was saying. He asked, "What do I need to do to get to live with Heavenly Father forever?"

Aaron told him, "If you really want to live with Heavenly Father, you need to pray. You need to get down on your knees and bow down before Him and beg His forgiveness."

Kings never bow down. Instead, lesser people bow down to kings. The High King was not used to bowing down before anyone. But he climbed off of his throne, knelt down, and began to pray.

The High King prayed, "Heavenly Father, Aaron has taught me about you. I need to know for myself that you are real. Please show me that you are real and tell me what I must do to repent of my sins."

When the king said that, he was overcome by the Spirit and fainted. His servants thought he was dead and ran to tell the queen.

The queen did not know what had happened. She saw her husband lying on the ground surrounded by Aaron and his friends. She decided that her husband had been killed by Nephites. She ordered the servants to arrest Aaron and his friends. She

wanted them to die for killing her husband.

The servants had seen what had happened between Aaron and the king. They were afraid of the strange Nephites. They did not want to touch them.

When the queen saw that these brave servants were afraid of the Nephites, she began to be afraid. She ordered the servants to get the townspeople to come and help kill Aaron and his friends.

Aaron did not want a big fight in the castle. He did not want the queen to be afraid any more. He touched the High King. The king woke up. He stood and began to teach the queen and all of the other people in the room.

The High King had been taught many things by the Spirit of the Lord. He had been convinced that God was real. He knew that the Gospel was true. He wanted Aaron to teach all of the people in his kingdom. He wanted all of his people to learn the wonderful things he had been taught.

The king sent out a message to all of the Lamanites. This must have taken a long time, because there were a lot of Lamanites. The High King's kingdom was enormous. It stretched from one side of the continent to the other. It reached as far north as people lived, and as far south as it could until it reached the Nephites' land.

The High King told all of these people that Aaron, Omner, Himni, and their friends would be coming to teach them. The people were ordered to listen to these men and not hurt them.

Aaron and his brothers and friends began teaching. They went throughout the Lamanites' land. They taught group after group after group of people.

Some people listened. They prayed and learned more. Soon the church was growing and growing among the Lamanites.

_____

Why were the queen's servants afraid of Aaron?

Why was the king unconscious?

What did he learn?

Why did the church grow so quickly among the Lamanites?

Word Blocks

How do you build a testimony? Aaron taught us how! Put the mixed-up blocks into the grids below them to build phrases. These phrases are the steps we need to take to build a testimony.

Step 1:

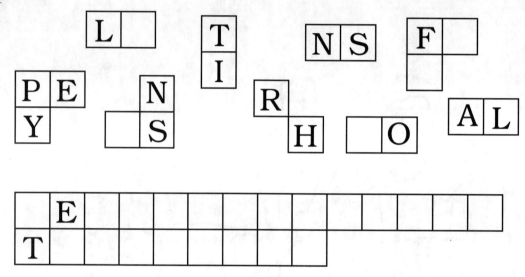

Step 2:

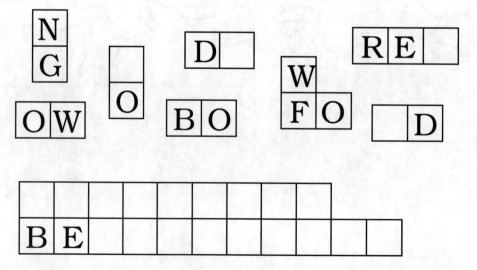

Step 3:

Step 4:

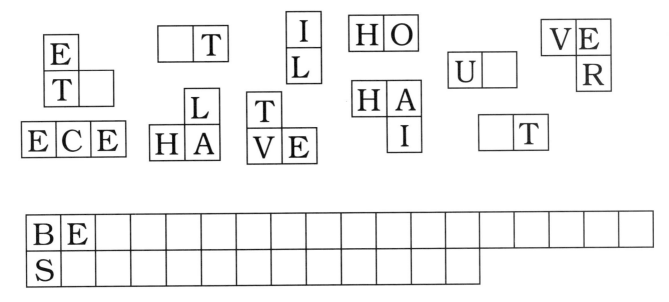

Step 5: Then shalt thou receive the hope which thou desirest. (Alma 22:16)

A Mighty Change

Alma 23; Jarom 1:6; Mosiah 9:12, 10:11-17, Enos 1:20

A miracle began to happen in the land of the Lamanites. It was the type of miracle that Heavenly Father often does: Lots of people worked and taught for a long time, and gradually the Church began to grow.

Do you remember what the Lamanites were like before Ammon, Aaron, Omner, and Himni met them?

They were a wild, ferocious people. Lehi taught his family about Heavenly Father, but by the time these Lamanites were born, they no longer believed in God. In fact, they believed that they had been betrayed by Nephi and Lehi.

They had taught their children to hate the Nephites and do all that they could to destroy them. The Lamanites had hated the Nephites for so many years that it was very difficult for them to change.

The High King sent Aaron, Omner, and Himni throughout the land of the Lamanites to teach them that they should leave the traditions of their fathers and become members of the Lord's church.

The missionaries began to have great success. Thousands of Lamanites were converted to the Gospel! Thousands of Lamanites became righteous people. Thousands were baptized.

They put away their weapons and did not fight any more. They began to work hard to take care of themselves, so that they would not need to steal. They became friends with the Nephites and began to learn from them.

The converted Lamanites changed so much that they wanted to take a new name. They wanted to distinguish themselves from those Lamanites who still lived the old way.

These righteous Lamanites decided to call themselves Anti-Nephi-Lehies. This was a strange name. Usually "anti-" means "opposed to", but in this case it seems to mean "to be like", as the opposing image in a mirror is "like" the image of the person in front of it.

From that time on, they were called by their new name and were no longer called Lamanites.

Why did the Lamanites hate the Nephites?

Why was it so hard for them to change?

Word Blocks

Circle one letter in each block to form a word going across. Each word is from the story on page 126. Write your answers in the blanks at the bottom of the page.

1.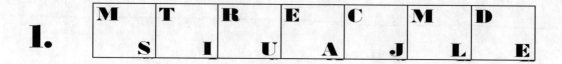

2.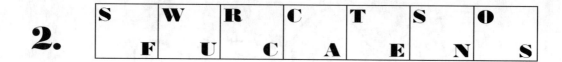

3.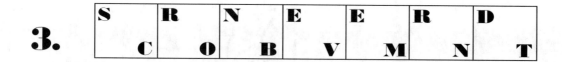

4.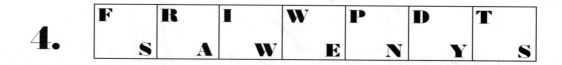

5.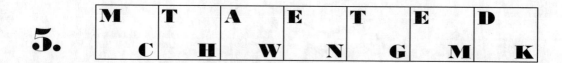

1._____   4._____

2._____

3._____   5._____

Code Circle

What happened to the Anti-Nephi-Lehies? Skip every
other letter around the circle to find out.

Start Here
↓

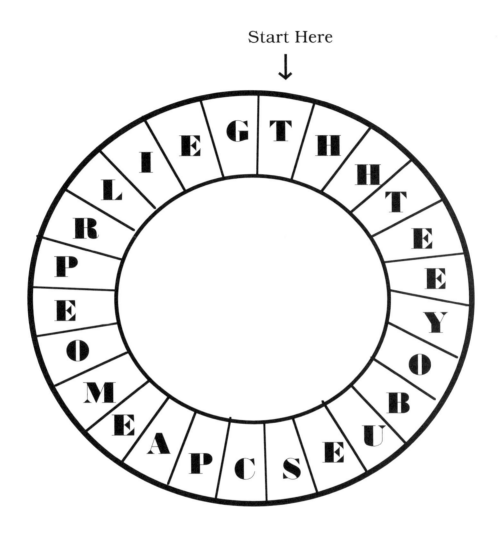

____ _____

_____

_____

The Honorable Anti-Nephi-Lehies

Alma 24

The Lamanites hated the Anti-Nephi-Lehies. They were jealous. The Anti-Nephi-Lehies worked hard and built nice houses. They had farms which produced lots of food. They had many things that the Lamanites were too lazy to make or grow.

Instead, the Lamanites wanted to take what the Anti-Nephi-Lehies had. They thought, "Why work hard when we can steal what we want?"

The Lamanites decided to attack the Anti-Nephi-Lehies. Ammon and his friends saw that the Lamanites were preparing for war. They quickly met with the righteous kings to decide what to do.

The Anti-Nephi-Lehies refused to fight. They had put away their weapons, and they did not want to fight any more. They decided that if they were killed in battle, at least they would die honorably. They had made a sacred promise to Heavenly Father, called a "covenant", that they would change their lives. They refused to break this promise, even if it meant getting killed.

The Anti-Nephi-Lehies decided to bury their weapons, not just put them away. They said, "We will bury them deep in the earth, that they may be kept bright, as a testimony that we have never used them."

The Lamanite army came closer and closer. The Anti-Nephi-Lehies knelt down in the road and began to pray. The Lamanites couldn't believe that these people weren't even going to fight back. They began killing.

They killed one thousand and five innocent people before they stopped. One thousand and five! After a while, even the Lamanites could not murder any more of these peaceful people.

The Lamanites put down their swords. Many of them repented of their sins and joined the Anti-Nephi-Lehies. In fact, more than a thousand Lamanites joined the Church. This was more than the number of people killed in the battle.

Sometimes the Lord works in unusual ways. In this case, a thousand people died so that more than a thousand people could be saved.

As the years passed, many more of the Lamanites heard the words of the missionaries and repented. They became Anti-Nephi-Lehies.

On the other hand, the rest of the Lamanites became more and more angry and violent. They hated the Anti-Nephi-Lehies and the Nephites. They decided that they would never change their ways. They became even more wild and wicked than before.

Ammon worried about his friends. He knew that the Lamanites would kill them if they could. Finally, he decided to move the entire group of Anti-Nephi-Lehies to the land of the Nephites. This way, the Nephites could protect them from the Lamanites.

Ammon went ahead of the group to warn the Chief Judge of the Nephites. He wanted to prepare the Nephites for their new citizens.

The Chief Judge sent a message throughout the Nephite cities. He wanted to know what the Nephites thought about the Anti-Nephi-Lehies.

When the messengers returned, they had a single message: All of the Nephites welcomed the Anti-Nephi-Lehies. They promised to defend and protect such a righteous people.

They gave the land of Jershon to the Anti-Nephi-Lehies to be their own land.

When the Anti-Nephi-Lehies arrived at the border of the Nephites' land, Ammon met them with the joyful news. The Anti-Nephi-Lehies rejoiced. Finally they would be able to live in peace!

They settled in the land of Jershon. They built new homes. They farmed the land and raised their families in peace.

The Nephites gave the Anti-Nephi-Lehies a new name. They called them "Ammonites", because they were brought to Jershon by Ammon. From that time on, the Book of Mormon calls these people "Ammonites".

The Ammonites chose to have the kind of government that the Nephites had. They elected Ammon to be their Chief Judge. They loved Ammon and wanted him to be their leader.

Why did Heavenly Father let so many good people be killed?

Was it worth it?

Could you have been as brave as the Anti-Nephi-Lehies?

Look It Up!

Look up Alma 24:16, 18 and fill in the missing words below. Then use the corresponding numbers to solve the puzzle on page 137.

16 And now, my brethren, if our brethren ___ ___ ___ ___
66 62 6 24
to destroy us, behold, we will ___ ___ ___ ___ away our
11 68 69 58
___ ___ ___ ___ ___ ___, yea,
81 21 82 23 89 37
even we will ___ ___ ___ ___
83 3 84 85
them deep in the ___ ___ ___ ___ ___, that they
42 31 19 10 2
may be kept bright, as a testimony that ___ ___ have never used
34 74
them, at the last day; and ___ ___ our brethren
70 53
___ ___ ___ ___ ___ ___ ___
64 9 43 14 90 18 36
us, behold, we shall go to our God and ___ ___ ___ ___ ___ be saved.
71 27 72 61 73

18   And this they did, it being in their view a ___ ___ ___ ___ ___ -
13 67 56 26 28
___ ___ ___ ___ to God, and
30 59 29 33
also to men, ___ ___ ___ ___
38 15 44 40
they never would use ___ ___ ___ ___ ___ ___ ___
5 25 12 57 52 51 7
again for the shedding of man's ___ ___ ___ ___ ___;
63 17 39 50 20
and this they did, vouching and ___ ___ ___ ___ ___-
75 22 76 8 77
___ ___ ___ ___ ___ ___ with
35 32 1 55 78 79
God, that rather ___ ___ ___ ___ shed the
48 41 47 80
blood of their brethren ___ ___ ___ ___ would
86 54 87 88
give ___ ___ their own
65 60
___ ___ ___ ___ ___ ___.
45 49 46 16 4

136

Can You Break the Code?

Use the letters and corresponding numbers from page 136 to
fill in the blanks. If you need help, see Alma 24:27

___ ___ ___ ___   ___ ___   ___ ___ ___
 1   2   3   4   5   6   7   8   9

___ ___ ___ ___   ___ ___ ___   ___ ___ ___ ___
10 11 12 13   14 15 16   17 18 19 20

___ ___ ___ ___ ___ ___ ___   ___ ___
21 22 23 24 25 26 27   28 29

___ ___ ___ ___   ___ ___ ___ ___
30 31 32 33   34 35 36 37

___ ___   ___ ___ ___
38 39   40 41 42

___ ___ ___ ___ ___ ___ ___ ___ ___
43 44 45 46 47 48 49 50 51

___ ___   ___ ___ ___
52 53   54 55 56

___ ___ ___   ___ ___ ___
57 58 59   60 61 62

Korihor the Anti-Christ

Alma 30

The Nephites had laws to make sure that their people were free. One of these laws said that anyone could say anything they wanted, and the government could not punish them.

There were a lot of people living in Zarahemla and the cities around it. That meant that there were a lot of opinions. Each person had a right to say what they believed.

A man named Korihor liked this law. He went throughout the land telling people that the prophets were wrong. He was an Anti-Christ. "Anti-" means "against", so an Anti-Christ is someone who works against Christ.

Korihor believed that there would be no Christ. He preached that when we die, we simply stop living. He said that we stop being anything at all.

Korihor said that no one could know if there was a Christ. He said that since we stopped existing after we die, there was no need for repentance. He said that there was no need for Jesus to die for our sins.

Korihor went to the land of Jershon to teach his ideas to the Ammonites. But the Ammonites were smart. They had faith in the things they had learned through the Spirit, and they refused to listen to the Anti-Christ.

Instead, they tied Korihor up and brought him to Ammon. Ammon made Korihor leave the land of Jershon.

Next, Korihor went to the land of Gideon. Again he was tied up and brought to the Chief Judge. This time the Chief Judge sent him to Alma in Zarahemla.

Korihor told his opinions to Alma and the Chief Judge. He told them that they were only trying to get the people's money.

Alma said, "You are being silly. You know that I have never taken money for my work. I have never received even one penny for all of the years I have served this people. I have always worked hard to earn my own money."

Then Alma proceeded to teach Korihor about Heavenly Father and Jesus. He asked, "Do you believe in God?"

Korihor answered, "No, I do not. And I do not believe there is a Christ."

Alma asked, "Can you prove that there is not a God? Can you prove that there is no Christ? I have only your word to tell me so.

"But I have everything around me to prove to me that there is a God. I have the earth, the moon, and the stars to prove to me that God is real. I have all of the plants and animals to show me God's power. To me, these things prove that God is real."

Korihor said, "If you will show me a sign, then I will believe you. Use your powers to do something that only the power of God could do."

Alma answered, "Okay, I'll give you a sign. From now on, you will not be able to hear or speak. This should prove to you that God is real."

When Alma said these words, Korihor was struck dumb. He couldn't hear or speak.

When the Chief Judge saw what had happened, he wrote a note to Korihor. The note said, "Now do you believe us? God has shown you a sign. Are you still going to argue with us?"

Korihor wrote back, "I know that only the power of God could make me unable to hear or speak. I admit that I always knew there was a God. Please pray for me, that God will lift this curse from me."

Alma said, "No. If you could speak again, you would teach bad things to the people again. If God wants you to speak, He will lift the curse himself."

Korihor remained dumb. He was cast out of the city. He became a beggar and went from house to house begging for food. One day, he was run over in the street and died. How sad that such a smart man could be so silly! His stubborn ways made Heavenly Father punish him, and he died still being sad and stubborn.

_____

What is an anti-christ?

What proves to you that God is real?

How can you strengthen your testimony?

Look It Up!

Look up Alma 30:43-44 and fill in the missing words below.
Then find those words in the Word Search on the next page.

43 And now _____ said unto _____: If thou wilt show me a _____, that I may be _____ that there is a God, yea, show unto me that he hath _____, and then will I be convinced of the _____ of thy words.

44 But Alma said unto him: Thou hast had signs enough; will ye _____ your God? Will ye say, _____ unto me a sign, when ye have the _____ of all these thy _____, and also all the holy _____? The _____ are laid before thee, yea, and all things denote there is a God; yea, even the _____, and all _____ that are upon the face of it, yea, and its _____, yea, and also all the _____, which move in their _____ do _____ that there is a _____ _____.

Word Search

Look for the words you wrote on page 142. Can you find all of them? Remember--words can be written forward, backward, and diagonally.

```
G R F T X Q S C R I P T U R E S K H E A
N K X Q E W C P T D V I Z Y S A U I M H
I B D I U S Q Y O D N R I N Y F A C P Z
R S X X B Z T M O Y C X F X O U G J L L
I I D M S G N I H T T K R T J A A M A M
C K R W N T R T M F N K E H M E A A N X
U O G A E O H O K O K Y D L Z R G K E Q
F R B Q R N S T N N E A B R V F X T E
R I G Q H O K E Q A C Y P G A D Y E S M
Z H T C T Y N T M N E S N L L O X G K E
C O O H E F I Z I P S R W M U Z W T Z R
U R A T R F V V R O T I C N G J V I W P
H H E U B B N H F E T Z N M E G X E W U
L I X R O O W J E B J U E Q R B V F Y S
W E A T C P M J Y G R Z D J V V F J I I
S I G N A J O R A W O H S T E H P O R P
G B Z F W X M Q P R S D D Y M X T P S N
V M J N M O T I O N A L T Q P M B O N H
F S S E N T I W O R P O W E R F L D T Y
K F U M A D H T R A E C Y J F S D G K B
```

The Ammonites

Alma 27

The Lamanites did not remain peaceful for long. Again and again they attacked the Anti-Nephi-Lehies.

Ammon and his brothers loved the Anti-Nephi-Lehies. The missionaries could not bear to see the destruction of such righteous people.

Ammon asked the king if he would move his people near the Nephites' land. Then the Nephites could protect the Anti-Nephi-Lehies.

But the king remembered all of the horrible things he and his brethren had done to the Nephites before their conversion. He was afraid that the Nephites would still be angry and try to kill them.

Ammon said, "I will pray about this. If the Lord tells you to go, will you do it?"

The king said, "I will do anything the Lord tells me to do."

So Ammon went and prayed for help. The Lord told him to take the Anti-Nephi-Lehies far away from the wicked Lamanites. He told Ammon to take the helpless people to the land of the Nephites.

The Anti-Nephi-Lehies gathered their families, their animals, and their crops. They began the difficult journey to the land of the Nephites.

Ammon went ahead of them to warn the Chief Judge of the Nephites. He wanted to prepare the Nephites for their new citizens.

The Chief Judge sent a message throughout the Nephite cities. He wanted to know what the Nephites thought about the Anti-Nephi-Lehies.

When the messengers returned, they had a single message: All of the Nephites welcomed the Anti-Nephi-Lehies. They promised to defend and protect such a righteous people. They gave the land of Jershon to the Anti-Nephi-Lehies to be their own land.

When the Anti-Nephi-Lehies arrived at the border of the Nephites' land, Ammon met them with joyful news. The Anti-Nephi-Lehies rejoiced. Finally they could live in peace!

They settled in the land of Jershon. They built new homes. They farmed the land and raised their families in peace.

The Nephites gave the Anti-Nephi-Lehies a new name. They called them "Ammonites", because they were brought to Jershon by Ammon. From that time on, the Book of Mormon calls these people "Ammonites".

The Ammonites chose to have the kind of government that the Nephites had. They elected Ammon to be their Chief Judge. They loved Ammon and wanted him to be their leader.

Why didn't the Anti-Nephi-Lehies want to fight any more?

Why did they change their name to "Ammonites"?

Maze

Begin drawing at the arrow and continue
until you reach the end. What do you see?

The Silly Zoramites

Alma 31-32

The Zoramites lived in a city near Zarahemla. They were very silly people. They were a rich and prosperous people, but they had begun to worship God in a strange way.

Every Sabbath, each Zoramite climbed to the top of a high, high tower. Then he would lift his arms into the air and shout a prayer. Each prayer was the same as the others. When the prayer was finished, the next person would climb the tower and shout his prayer.

Then the Zoramites would go about their business the rest of the week. They only thought about God on Sundays.

The Zoramites were a proud people. They wore fine clothes. They loved beautiful jewelry. They felt that the best people were the ones who had the most beautiful things.

Not all of the Zoramites were so silly. Some of the Zoramite people were poor and could not dress as beautifully as the rich people. The rich Zoramites would not let the poor ones into the churches or let them pray.

The poor people felt like they had no way to worship. They were very sad. These people were humble. They didn't have pretty clothes, fancy foods, or lots of money. Being poor made them be humble.

Alma and Amulek came to the Zoramite's city. They saw what was happening. They thought that the rich Zoramites were very silly and quite mean.

Alma and Amulek started preaching the Gospel. No one would listen to them. They were a little discouraged. They went to a hill on the edge of the city and began to preach to some of the poor people there.

Alma told the poor people that they would be blessed for their humility. Then he added, "But it would be much better if you could be humble for other reasons. You would be blessed even more if you were humble because you loved Heavenly Father and wanted to keep His commandments."

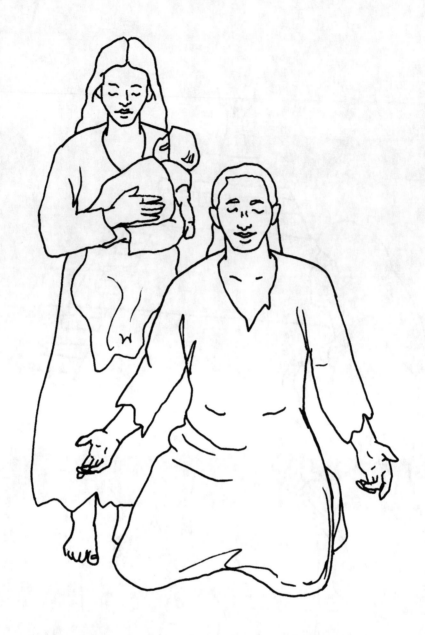

The poor Zoramites listened to what Alma and Amulek had to say. They were happy when they found out that they didn't have to go to the tower on Sundays to pray. They could pray anywhere and any time they wanted!

The poor Zoramites also were happy to know that Heavenly Father doesn't judge us according to what we have. He doesn't care if we have fine clothes. He only cares about us being good.

The poor Zoramites wanted to learn more.

Why did the silly Zoramites pray on top of the tower?

Why were the poor Zoramites humble?

Who can pray? Why?

Elimination

Read each clue and cross out the picture it describes.
The pictures that are left will make a sentence.

Clues:

1. This grows on a tree.
2. This makes a yummy lunch.
3. This says, "Woof!"
4. These make you run faster.
5. This is fun to open.

Seeds of Faith

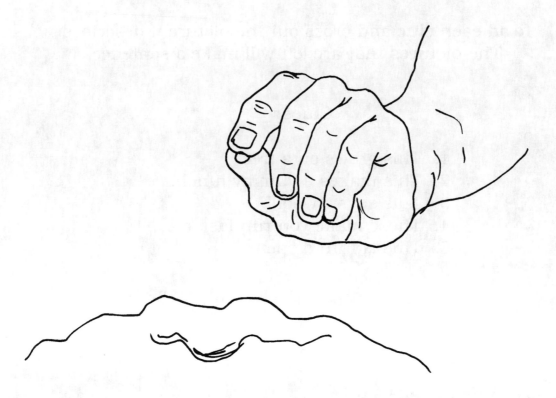

Alma 32-33

Alma and Amulek taught the Zoramites many great things. Alma gave a speech about faith that is famous. It is famous because it teaches us how to make our faith stronger.

The poor Zoramites had lots of questions. They weren't sure that there really was a God. They didn't know if anyone was listening to their prayers.

Alma asked the Zoramites to do an experiment. He told them to have faith in what he was teaching them. He told them to have faith in Heavenly Father.

Alma told the Zoramites to think of faith as a seed. A seed is little and round. It doesn't look like a plant. But if a seed is watered and fed, it can grow into a large, beautiful plant.

Alma told the Zoramites (and us) to treat our faith like a little seed. We should "plant" it in our hearts by deciding to find out if God is real. We should "water" it by learning as much as we can about Him.

If the "seed", or knowledge of God, is true, then it will begin to grow within our hearts. We will learn more about about Heavenly Father, and He will

use the Holy Ghost to answer our questions.

As the "plant", our knowledge of the Gospel, grows, we will grow in our understanding of Heavenly Father. The more we "feed" it by learning about Him, the larger the "plant" will grow. We will learn more and more about God and He will teach us whether what we have learned is correct.

Alma says that our knowledge of the Gospel can grow as large as a tree! If we take care of our "tree" by learning and praying, our "tree" will stay healthy. It will bear "fruit", or blessings, because we kept the commandments.

In other words, we will receive blessings from our experiment. When we pray and learn, we grow spiritually. If we use prayer and study to help our little bit of knowledge grow larger, the Lord will bless us for our faithfulness.

How is faith like a seed? How does it "grow"?

Alma said we could "try" (test) his words. How would you "test" him if he said you would be blessed if you say your prayers?

If you go to church?

If you say kind words to every person?

Scrambled Sentences

What can you do to help your "seed" of faith grow? Unscramble
the sentences below to find some ideas.

1. ARPY   EEYRV   AYD

   _ _ _ _   _ _ _ _ _   _ _ _

2. DRAE   ETH   PURSETRCSI

   _ _ _ _   _ _ _   _ _ _ _ _ _ _ _ _

3. OG   OT   MRIARPY

   _ _   _ _   _ _ _ _ _ _

4. PYA   YM   HGITTNI

   _ _ _   _ _   _ _ _ _ _ _

5. AERB   YM   IONMYSTTE

   _ _ _ _   _ _   _ _ _ _ _ _ _ _

6. ERANL TUBOA LHAENVEY HRETAF

   _

What Do You Think?

On page 154, we gave you some ideas for growing your faith. What do you plan to do? Write your goals on the lines below. When you are done, hold the page up to the light to see what has happened to your faith already!

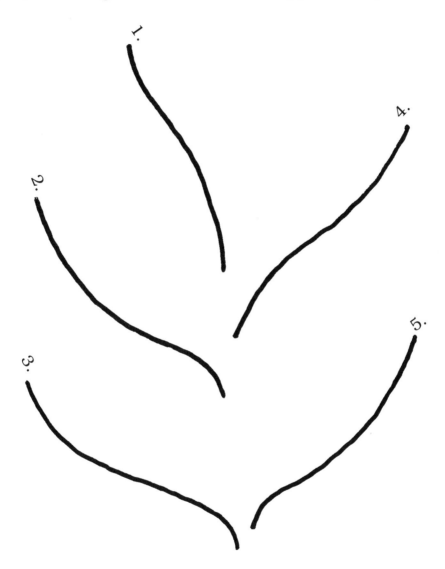

Complete the Sentence

Can you fill in the missing parts of the letters below?
What does the sentence say?

MY FAITH CAN GROW
AS BIG AS A TREE.

Fatherly Advice

Alma 36-42, 45

Alma was a great prophet. He was a great missionary. He was also a great father. He loved his children and wanted them to have all of the blessings that the Gospel could bring to them.

Alma had three sons. Their names were Helaman, Shiblon, and Corianton. These young men were like most brothers: Each one was different, and each made his own decisions.

Alma was getting old. He wanted to give his sons some advice before he died. He met with them one at a time and told each son what the young man needed to know.

Helaman was the oldest son. Alma talked to him first. He said, "Helaman, you have made me proud. You keep the commandments. You always choose the right. You have been a good missionary. The Lord is happy with you."

Then Alma told his son about the angel appearing to him. He said, "I was unconscious for three days. During those three days, I repented of my sins. I learned that Christ will come to earth. He will die to atone for our sins. Because of His sacrifice, we will be able to live with Heavenly Father some day."

Alma asked, "Do you remember the Liahona? It guided our fathers through the wilderness. The Gospel is like the Liahona. It guides us back to our Heavenly Father."

Shiblon was next. Alma called him in and said to him, "You have also been a good son. You have suffered many times because you preached the Gospel. Heavenly Father has seen your trials, and He will bless you for your efforts."

Then Alma told Shiblon what a good son he was. He said, "I am proud of you because you make such good decisions. You choose the right. You keep the commandments. You have been a faithful missionary. I know that if you continue to do these things, Heavenly Father will give you many blessings. You will be happy because of your good decisions."

After Alma talked to Shiblon, he talked to Corianton. Corianton had not made good decisions. He went on a mission, but he did not preach the Gospel. Instead, he and his friends did bad things. Alma was very unhappy with him.

Alma told him, "Corianton, you need to repent. You have done many bad things. You have made bad decisions. Because of your actions, many people want to do what you do. Because of your example, they don't want to keep the commandments. You have not helped the Lord."

Then Alma said, "I know that you can do better. If you will keep the commandments, the Lord will bless you. I know that you will be happier if you will make good decisions instead of bad ones. You will never be happy if you continue being wicked. I know that you are strong, and you can turn your life around. Heavenly Father will help you."

After Alma finished saying these things to his sons, all four men went back among the Zoramites to do missionary work. All of them worked very hard, even Corianton. Many people listened to them and were baptized.

Some time later, Alma left Zarahemla to go to the city of Melek. He never reached Melek. Many people thought that because was such a good man, God had taken him up to heaven without dying, like He had done with the prophet Elijah.

We know nothing about Alma's death, but we know much about his life. He was a great prophet who taught us many wonderful truths.

Why was Alma so worried about Corianton?

What could Corianton do to turn his life around?

Does Heavenly Father forgive everyone?

What Do You Think?

What do you think Alma looked like? What did Corianton look like? Draw a picture of them in the square below.

General Moroni

Alma 43-44, 48

The Lamanites were getting ready for war. Their leader, Zerahemnah, hated the Nephites. He believed all of the things that his fathers believed about the Nephites. Zerahemnah wanted to make the Nephites into slaves. He wanted to have power over them. He wanted to make them pay for all of the bad things he thought they had done.

Many of the Lamanites hated the Nephites as much as Zerahemnah did. Zerahemnah used these men for leaders in his army. He wanted his soldiers to be as angry as he was. The leaders repeated Zerahemnah's words to the soldiers until the entire Lamanite army wanted to destroy the Nephites.

The Nephites had a serious problem: If the Lamanites were to defeat them, they would not be able to worship as they chose. They would have to follow the laws made by the Lamanites.

When the Lamanite army came near the Nephites' land, the Nephite army was ready. The Lamanites had twice as many soldiers as the Nephites had, but the Nephites had General Moroni for their leader.

Moroni armed his people with every type of weapon available to him. He also did something very smart: he made sure that his soldiers had thick leather clothes, a shield over their chests, a larger shield to hold in their hand, and a helmet.

The Lamanites wore almost no clothes. They wore only a little strip of leather around their waist, called a "loincloth". They had swords and spears, but no clothing to protect their bodies. They had no shields or helmets.

When the Lamanite soldiers saw the Nephites' armor, they were afraid. They knew that they could not fight armored soldiers and win. They turned around and marched away from the Nephites. They hoped that the Nephite army would not know where they were going to hide.

General Moroni was smart. He sent half of his army after the Lamanites. He sent the other half of his soldiers in the opposite direction. They went around the city and met the Lamanites on the other side.

The Lamanites were trapped. They had half of the Nephite army behind them, and half in front of them. They tried to fight, but so many of them died that they soon had to give up.

The Nephites were protected by their armor, but the Lamanites were almost naked. Very few Nephites were killed, but many, many Lamanites died in the battle. Soon Moroni ordered his men to stop fighting.

The Lamanites surrendered. Moroni told Zerahemnah, "The Lord has delivered you into our hands. You are angry at us because of our religion, but our God has saved us. You cannot destroy us or our faith."

Moroni made the Lamanites promise not to fight any more. Then he took their weapons and let them go home.

Moroni knew that the war was not over. He did not believe that the Lamanites would keep their promise. He went back to Zarahemla and prepared for more battles.

_____

Why did Moroni prepare for more battles?

Moroni is famous for fighting with his brain so that fewer of his men died in battle. What smart things did he do?

Word Search

```
G R S X D U E H U T T D M M H M Y P I N
Z R A M T J P A Q V C Y T C N L N U T A
W K V P F J J S C Z V I G N O V L H X U
H O G L O N T O B G C W U D M X R R D G
J L C N V K H Y P S E P C U P V A I L C
K K Z S Y P X K U T B B I G N X R Z A B
M A G P A U S O L D I E R S B F M W O G
B K O N G W A A K R D M R E Q S O T N V
L E L M Z E R A H E M N A H T R R D I C
G H L K T A I X S L A V E S R B Y Z E G
X T F X S E I V C U J J I O X C N L F U
T O K H I C E K P B H F N R X K A Q J X
F L T P K H N T A Q L P O V I J T G J S
N C D I R I Q D G U T N R Z D N Z R G E
Z N X A C S B H B W H I O I L O B W X T
A I W P H H J B J Z S M E E W K B Y I
F O A E L A M A N I T E S B I J Y X H H
U L R T C K H Y I H M D P K H G B C H P
U Z P H L P M C V X S U X A S B V L I E
Q A Y I W O R E G T E M L E H J X I C N
```

ARMOR
HELMET
LAMANITES
LOINCLOTH
MORONI

NEPHITES
SHIELD
SLAVES
SOLDIERS
WAR
ZERAHEMNAH

Preventative Measures

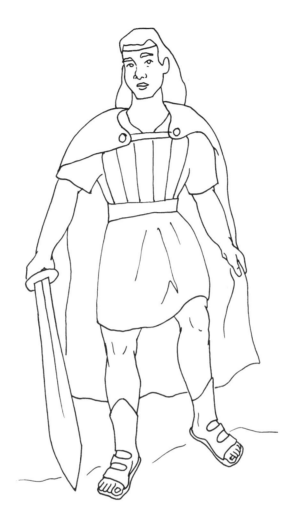

Alma 45-48

General Moroni was smart. He knew that his army won the last battle because they had armor. He also knew that the next time the Lamanite army attacked, the Lamanite soldiers would also have armor. This meant that the Nephites would have to think of some other way to protect themselves.

The Nephites were not trying to attack the Lamanites. They were simply trying to protect their homes, their families, and their freedom. They had to find a way to protect their cities.

Moroni and his men built small forts at the edges of the Nephites' land. They built stone walls around the cities. They mounded dirt around the stone walls. They did everything they could do to prepare for war.

When the forts and walls were done, Moroni's army was ready. They waited for the next battle to begin.

_____

What smart things did General Moroni do?

Why is it important to learn about him?

Hidden Words

The Lamanites lived in the Land of Nephi. Where did the Nephites live? Solve this puzzle by crossing out any letter which appears four times. Write the letters that are left in the blanks below. They will spell out the name of the Nephites' home.

W T Y C H P W E G Y S R
Y C L G A P M R S M W N
C D B P O R C M U G N
W T P Y I F S U R L G M S

__ __ __

__ __ __ __

__ __ __ __ __ __ __ __ __

The Title of Liberty

Alma 46

While Moroni prepared for trouble outside Nephite land, bad men were causing trouble inside Zarahemla. A man named Amalickiah wanted to be the king of the Nephites.

Amalickiah knew how to use tricky words to convince people to do what he wanted. He talked to large crowds of people. Soon these people wanted to help him. They thought he would be a good king. They wanted to get rid of the judges and make Amalickiah their king. Amalickiah's followers were called "kingmen".

Most of the Nephites did not want a king. They wanted to keep their judges in power. They wanted to be free. They called themselves "free-men".

The kingmen and the freemen argued and argued. Soon they began fighting each other. There was so much fighting that a war almost started in Zarahemla.

General Moroni heard what was happening. He couldn't believe that his people could be so stupid. They needed to work together to fight the Lamanites, and they were wasting time and energy fighting each other!

Moroni took off his coat and tore it in half. He painted words on one half of the coat and fastened it to a long stick. The banner said, "In memory of our God, our religion, and freedom, and our peace, our wives, and our children."

Moroni called his flag the "Title of Liberty". The message written on it showed what he and his men were fighting to protect: their religion, their freedom, and their families.

General Moroni raised the Title of Liberty high in the air and marched into the city. He invited all of the people to make a promise to God that they would only fight to defend their religion, freedom, and families. They also promised to keep the commandments. In return, they had faith that God would protect and bless them.

Many, many people followed Moroni. They took off their coats and tore them in half. They cried, "The Lord may tear us in half like these coats if we don't keep our promises to Him."

General Moroni gathered freemen from all of the Nephite cities. They decided to force the kingmen either to fight or surrender. Moroni had such a large group of freemen that Amalikiah was afraid. He and the kingmen turned and ran into the wilderness.

General Moroni and the freemen chased the kingmen. Amalikiah escaped with a few friends, but the freemen captured the rest of the kingmen.

The freemen asked each kingman if he would support the cause of freedom. Any kingman who would not make the freemen covenant of obedience to God and country was put to death. Most of the kingmen promised to fight only for righteous reasons and keep the commandments.

General Moroni raised the Title of Liberty on the towers and walls of every city in the Nephite lands. It flew there, a reminder to the Nephites of their promises to Heavenly Father.

_____

What does "Title of Liberty" mean?

Why would Moroni choose that title?

Why did the Nephites fight?

Is it wicked to fight for those reasons?

What Do You Think?

General Moroni posted the Title of Liberty on every tower in the Nephite lands. What do you think it looked like? Draw your ideas below. To find which words to write on it, look up Alma 46:12-13.

On and On

Alma 48-52

The war between the Nephites and the Lamanites went on for many years. The Lamanites attacked again and again, and the Nephites defended their religion, freedom, and families.

General Moroni worked hard. He directed his men to build more and more forts and strongholds. He put large groups of soldiers in places that had previously been weak spots in the Nephite defense.

Moroni's men built forts where the Lamanites were most likely to attack. They piled large mounds of dirt around the forts and built fences on top of the dirt. Then they fastened spiked pieces of wood to the top of the fences.

Most importantly, Moroni was a very good man who always prayed for guidance. Heavenly Father answered these prayers and told him where the Lamanites were planning to attack. As a result, when the Lamanites arrived at a Nephite city, Moroni would be there already with his army.

Each time the Lamanites attacked, the Nephite soldiers fought back and won. Many Nephites died, but thousands of Lamanites died in these battles. This made the Nephites sad, because they didn't like killing. The fighting went on and on.

_____

What smart things did Moroni do this time? Did God help him? How?

Can You Break the Code?

Substitute letters for the symbols, using the key on the next page. When you are done, check your answers by looking up Alma 48:10

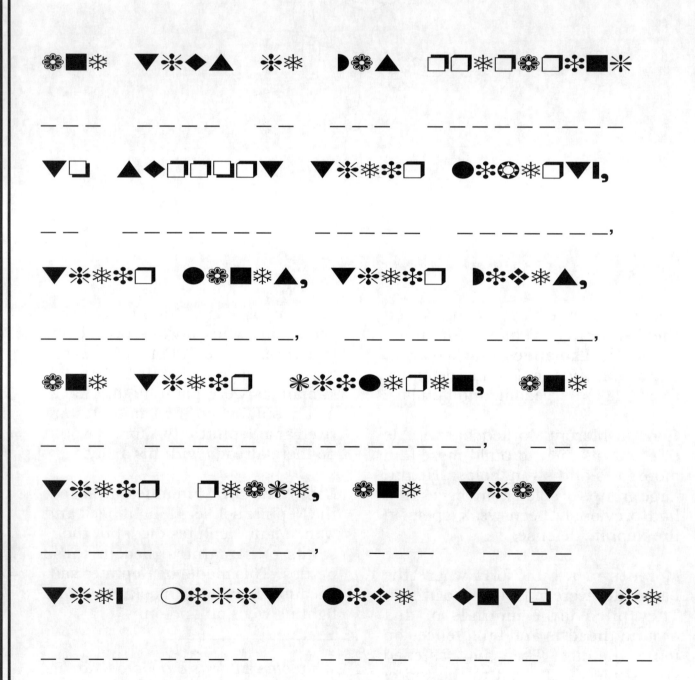

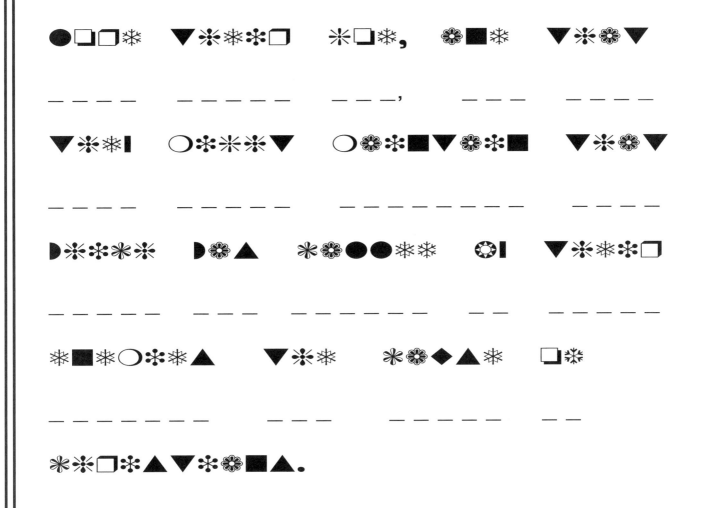

A = ❀ J = ✵ S = ▲

B = ☻ K = ✳ T = ▼

C = ❋ L = ● U = ◆

D = ❄ M = ○ V = ❖

E = ❅ N = ■ W = ◗

F = ❆ O = ❑ X = |

G = ✳ P = ◗ Y = ▐

H = ❄ Q = ❑ Z = ▮

I = ✻ R = ❒

173

Marching to Battle

Alma 53

The Ammonites were Lamanites who were converted by Ammon, the son of Mosiah. They called themselves "Anti-Nephi-Lehies" until they had to leave the land of the Lamanites. Ammon brought them to the land of the Nephites so that the Nephites could protect them. They changed their name to "Ammonites".

When the Ammonites joined the Church, they repented of the many times they had hurt or killed innocent people. The Ammonites buried their weapons and promised Heavenly Father that they would never kill again. The Nephites respected this promise and agreed to protect the people of Ammon if they would give the Nephite soldiers food and shelter.

As the war with the Lamanites dragged on and on, the Ammonites could see that the Nephites needed help. Many Nephite soldiers died while defending the Ammonites. The people of Ammon gave as much food and money to the army as they possibly could, but they felt that they needed to do more.

The Ammonites met and talked about what to do. They reluctantly decided to get weapons and join the Nephite army.

Helaman, the son of Alma, was the prophet at this time. He did not want the Ammonites to break their promise to Heavenly Father. He begged the people of Ammon not to fight.

But the Ammonites still wanted to help the Nephites who had been so kind to them. They met again to decide what to do. Finally they had an idea.

The Ammonites had many sons who were born after their parents joined the Church. These children had never taken an oath not to fight. Only their parents had actually made that promise. The Ammonites had raised their sons to be peaceful, but now the situation had changed.

It had not been many years since the Ammonites' conversion, so the children who had not made the promise were quite young. They probably were not more than fifteen years old,

yet they were willing to join the Nephite army and fight for freedom.

The adult Ammonites were afraid that their young sons would be killed in battle. But they knew that the Nephites needed help, and they decided to send their sons in spite of their fears.

Helaman prayed for guidance in this matter. Heavenly Father promised him and the worried parents that not one boy would die in the war. It took a lot of faith, but the Ammonites let their precious sons go.

There were two thousand of these young fighters. They asked Helaman to be their commander. Helaman agreed, and with the Lord's prophet as their leader, they set out for the battle front.

The Ammonites had been a weak spot in the Nephite forces. Now they were a strength, and this strength came at a time when the Nephites really needed help. General Moroni gratefully accepted the services of these exceptional young men.

Why did the Ammonites let their sons fight?

What prepared these boys for battle?

What advantages did they have?

Hidden Words

Can you find the names hidden in the sentences below? Underline the letters that form the names. The first one is done for you.

Manti, Nephi, Lehi, and Provo are towns in Utah.

The L.A. manager was a really nice guy.

To Sam, Mondays were absolute nightmares.

Armor on its own is not an adequate defense.

Located near the state line, Philadelphia is close to three states.

Please tell Michelle "Hi" for me.

Mom is baking me nine cakes for my birthday.

The prisoner shouted, "Free me now!"

Next Thursday is our annual magic show.

Last week a mule kicked my little brother.

Need help? Look for these words:

Helaman	Amulek	Kingmen
Ammon	Lehi	Alma
Moroni	Nephi	Anti-Nephi-Lehi
Freemen		

Helaman's Sons

Alma 53, 56-57

Helaman loved his young soldiers. They were such wonderful boys that Helaman thought of them as his own sons.

In his letters to Moroni, Helaman called the young men "my little sons" and "my two thousand stripling warriors". He did not want even one of these precious children to get hurt. Even though he worried, he had faith that the Lord would keep His promise to protect them.

As for the boys, they were not afraid. Their mothers had taught them that God would take care of them. They had so much faith that they were not afraid of any task. They bravely marched into battle and fought as hard as they could.

The Lamanites had taken several of the Nephite cities which were closest to the Lamanites' land. The Lamanites treated the people who lived in these cities as slaves. They were cruel to their Nephite prisoners.

A man named Antipus was the commander of the Nephite army in this area. He had lost many soldiers in previous battles, so he was very happy to see Helaman's two thousand soldiers.

The Lamanite army had taken enough territory in this area that they were able to use the captured cities to strengthen its forces. After all, the cities had enough food and slaves to take care of lots and lots of Lamanite

soldiers. In this way, the Lamanite army grew stronger and stronger.

Antipus knew that he had to get those cities back at any cost. He and his soldiers decided to fight until they captured the lost territory, even though many Nephites would die in the battle. They were willing to die if necessary, because they believed that freedom was worth dying for.

The Lamanites were protected by the walls and forts which Moroni's sol-diers had built. Antipus knew how difficult it would be to attack the Lamanites while they were inside the Nephite strongholds.

Antipus decided to trick the Lamanites into leaving the cities. He ordered Helaman's forces to march to a Nephite city nearby. They were to appear as if they were carrying supplies to the people in the city. On their journey, they would pass the city which held the largest part of the Lamanite army.

The two thousand young soldiers obediently marched right past the Lamanite army. Lamanite spies immediately discovered them, and the Lamanites marched very fast to capture the Nephite soldiers and supplies.

When Helaman's warriors saw the approaching Lamanites, they turned and marched even more quickly from the city, into the wilderness. The Lamanites followed. Both armies traveled as quickly as possible, until they were far into the woods.

The young fighters had tricked the Lamanite army! Without any fighting, they had led the strongest of the Lamanite forces away from its stronghold. Antipus and his men marched into the city and killed the remaining Lamanite guards. The city was once again Nephite territory.

Antipus knew he needed to help Helaman's stripling warriors. The Lamanite army still chased them and would kill them if they caught them. Antipus and his men left a few soldiers to guard the city and ran into the woods.

When the Lamanite commander saw that the Nephite army was chasing him, he ordered his men to run even faster toward Helaman's forces. He knew that if he did not catch them and kill them quickly, his soldiers would be surrounded by Nephites. He wanted to get rid of the young soldiers before he had to fight the rest of the Nephite forces. He knew that he could not win if he had to fight both groups of Nephites at the same time.

The Lamanites ran and ran. So did Helaman and his "sons". Antipus and his men chased all of them.

Helaman looked back and saw that the Lamanites were no longer chasing them. He did not know if the Lamanites were trying to trick him, or if they had stopped to fight Antipus' men. If he turned around, would he and his boys walk into a trap? He didn't want his "sons" to get hurt.

Why did Antipus need to take back the Nephite cities?

What happened to the people in those cities when the Lamanites conquered them?

Antipus knew that many of his soldiers would be killed if he continued to fight the Lamanites. Why was it worth the cost to him?

Hidden Words

Cross out any letter which appears five or more times.
What is the secret message? What does it mean?

B	H	S	M	E	C	J	T	E
H	K	U	R	K	I	F	M	P
U	L	V	F	J	C	I	B	N
G	C	H	J	G	U	F	V	W
U	M	A	E	M	B	H	R	K
K	V	F	X	R	C	X	K	E
B	J	I	X	O	M	X	V	F
C	U	X	R	H	V	J	S	B

Brave Boys

Alma 53, 56-57

Helaman asked his boys what they thought he should do. The brave young men said, "Our mothers taught us that God will protect us when we obey. We have God's promise that we will not die in this battle. We want to turn around and fight the Lamanites."

Helaman had never seen such bravery and faith. He knew many great men, but he had never met anyone as strong and faithful as these two thousand young warriors. He turned his forces around and marched toward the Lamanites.

When Helaman and his soldiers found the Lamanites, they realized that they had arrived just in time. Antipus and his men were so tired from their journey that they hardly had the strength to fight. The Lamanites fought hard and killed many of these brave soldiers.

Helaman's forces joined the battle. The Lamanite army was surrounded, with Helaman's boys behind them and Antipus' men in front. The battle grew fierce.

The Lamanite commander saw that many, many of his soldiers had been killed. He knew that if he kept fighting, he and the rest of his men would die. He decided to surrender instead.

The Lamanite soldiers put down their weapons. The Nephites took the weapons, then took the Lamanites as prisoners of war.

After the battle was over, Helaman anxiously counted his "sons". To his great astonishment and relief, not a single boy had been killed! Most of them had been injured, but not one had died.

This was only the first of many battles for Helaman's stripling warriors. They fought bravely, because they knew that God was watching over them. Heavenly Father kept His promise: Not one of them died during the war.

What promise did Heavenly Father keep?

Why did the young men fight so bravely?

182

Look It Up!

Look up Alma 53:20-21 and use it to fill in the blanks below. Then find those words in the Word Search on the next page.

20 And they were all _____ men, and they were exceedingly _____ for _____, and also for _____ and _____; but behold, this was not all--they were _____ who were _____ at all _____ in whatso-ever _____ they were _____.

21 Yea, they were men of _____ and _____, for they had been _____ to _____ the _____ of _____ and to _____ _____ before him.

Word Search

On the previous page, you filled in words from Alma 53:20-21. Find those words in the Word Search below.

```
G U S E M I T U N C F J A X O P V W S F
M P A R X I U E L R O V D M I V W K J Y
N W J G S S E N R E B O S H C J T D G E
H T A R W B Q O N U R G E W R I M W O X
U L L F T B W P O J Q G V L Z G N R M T
C W Z Q K E J R I I Y Y F P B M C N S X
B Y T N Z K I E N T R U S T E D S F L V
T U M K W G L K E E P Q D V F C X B W V
A P S Q H Y G T Y O U N G W M J P S J C
U C G T I G G A O K C A Y P M I D E U O
G Q L V W E B H X G T W K A N M E N Y M
H Y R A K B O N V I Z V I M B G O F J M
T C P L D E L Q Y A B R L U D S G Y B A
E O S I K R M M N V R X V L T F T M N
F U D A M E S T R E N G T H J R Z I I D
T R U N S E X Z N E T W S W Z U E V G M
H A N T Z T R U T H X O M P X E V I O E
I G X A J E H T O C M F S M F V B T D N
N E F R K N F F S F V K H R U V Y C V T
G S D M C U K X T V C Q Z L M H W A A S
```

General Moroni

Alma 59 - 60

Moroni was desperate. He needed more soldiers immediately. The Lamanites attacked again and again, and they were winning. There were so many Lamanite soldiers that the Nephites simply couldn't hold them back.

As the battles raged on, more and more Nephite soldiers died. Moroni begged for help, but none arrived.

The Lamanites attacked the city of Nephihah. This was a big city, with lots of people living in it. Moroni's men had worked hard to build stone walls around it. It was a strong city.

The Lamanites had so many men that they were able to capture the city of Nephihah. Many, many Lamanites died in the battle, but their leaders were pleased anyway. This was an important victory. Now the Lamanites controlled a large part of the territory near Zarahemla.

General Moroni knew that once the Lamanites took Nephihah, it would be nearly impossible to recapture the city. He knew how strong the defenses were in Nephihah, since his men had built them.

Moroni was angry that the Nephites had lost such an important city simply because there were not enough soldiers in that part of the country. He couldn't believe that the Nephites had not sent help.

He decided to write a letter to Pahoran, the Chief Judge in Zarahemla. How could the Nephite leader ignore the needs of the men who were risking their lives to defend him?

The letter was not nice. Moroni was so angry that he didn't even try to be polite, even though he was writing to the ruler of his country. This is what the letter said:

Dear Pahoran,

I have a few complaints. My men have almost no food, clothing, or other supplies. We have tried not to complain about this, because we are loyal to you.

This time, however, your selfishness has caused the deaths of thousands of brave Nephites. You know that you are supposed to supply men and weapons to our forces, yet no help has arrived.

We lost the city of Nephihah because you have been so selfish and lazy. How dare you sit safely on your throne while good men die for you!

I demand to know why you have been so thoughtless. I demand to know your reasons for neglecting us. Even as I write this letter, your Nephite brothers are dying. I blame you for their deaths.

I think you are allowing this to happen so that you can gain power. If the Lamanites kill all of the freemen, then you will be able to become the king of the Nephites. You know that God will not help you in your quest.

I am Moroni, the leader of the Nephite army. I do not seek power. Instead, I serve God.

Can You Break the Code?

The Nephites were righteous, but many, many of them died. Why did the Lord allow such righteous people to die? Check out Moroni's answer below.
(For help, look up Alma 60:13)

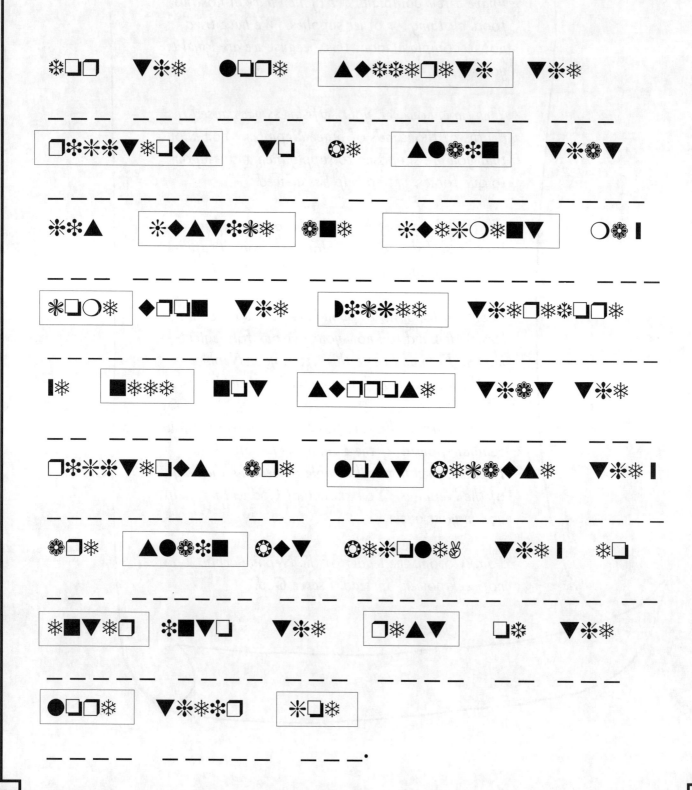

Crossword Puzzle

Use the words in the boxes on the previous page to fill the blanks in this crossword puzzle. The first answer is already in place.
The others can be figured from the first one.

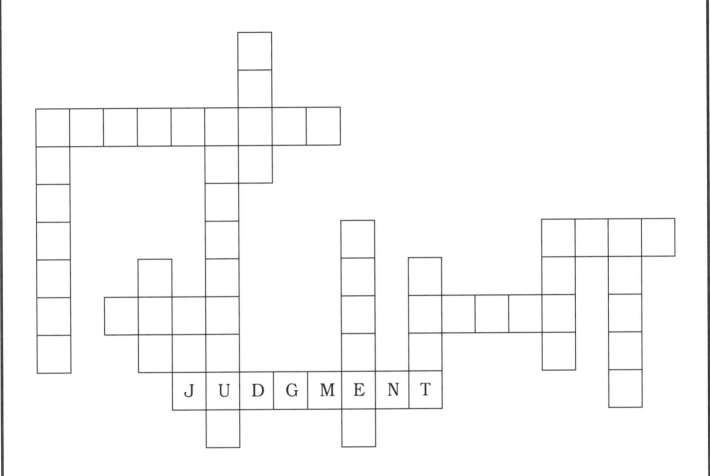

A = ✿	J = ☀	S = ▲
B = ✪	K = ✳	T = ▼
C = ❇	L = ●	U = ◆
D = ❄	M = ○	V = ❖
E = ❋	N = ■	W = ◗
F = ❄	O = ❏	X = ▏
G = ✻	P = ❐	Y = ▌
H = ❈	Q = ❑	Z = ◢◣
I = ✾	R = ❒	

Pahoran's Reply

Alma 61-62

If the leader of your country received a letter like Moroni's, how would they react? Would they get mad? Would they punish such a rude commander?

Pahoran was a good leader. He was also a remarkably kind and patient man. Instead of getting angry, he wrote a gentle letter back to Moroni asking for his help:

My Dear General Moroni,

I am sorry to hear about your troubles. I mourn with you because of the deaths of our brothers.

Some of the people here in Zarahemla were glad to hear about your losses. The kingmen are trying once again to take over the Nephite government. Your troubles have given them courage. There has been so much fighting here that I have been unable to help you. The kingmen have taken over Zarahemla. I was able to escape and am writing to you from the land of Gideon.

I have some men with me, but not enough to recapture Zarahemla. The people who live in this area are loyal freemen, however. They have fought so fiercely that the kingmen are afraid to leave Zarahemla.

I know that you are suffering, but we desperately need your help. We need to recapture Zarahemla before the Lamanite army arrives. If the Lamanites get here before you do, I am afraid that we will not be able to defeat them.

Thank you for being such a loyal commander. Now I end my letter to you, my beloved brother Moroni.

190

Word Search

```
E A H K B B Y R I Y P E S W Q K O M R B
E Y Y A J O K Z Z E K I N G M E N H F U
H J N L O C U K V E M S L T R Z I S E X
Z N K M A O T T J S U Q S A L Z E Y I P
E Y M E A P N J D Q O D T F A A O O X P
F X K H B B D G C O E L B Q Y H M B J P
G B W A O T V J E O D W D K O R O K T K
R G D R S O E O M N M H K I L V R I D B
T O L A V N X C T I T X P E E M O N E R
L H T Z T I N T W O X L L S J R N D N E
R P N P S R D H B U C F E Q W Z I H W T
N T A W O W R Y C X E Y W H I D T H U T
F Q E H R B U W J S A V F C N Z L S I E
I D F A O J D U L F R E E M E N E Y F L
A Q X H M R P E Q V W H M L W N M O G V
B N I O A D A Y Y I N E G Z B C Y H C Y
O D S C G M H N K J L L N V S K R M H Q
F S X P A T I E N T B I O G P X F T I Z
V M C G C W B K W Y D Y W L E E K F E T
O F J U G V G G P V S F M V X D O U D G
```

FREEMEN	MORONI
GENTLE	PAHORAN
KIND	PATIENT
KINGMEN	SOLDIER
LETTER	ZARAHEMLA
LOYAL	

Moroni to the Rescue

Alma 62

When Moroni received Pahoran's letter, he was filled with joy because he realized that he had misjudged Pahoran. Pahoran was a very good and righteous man but could not send supplies because of all the problems the unrighteous kingmen had caused in Zarahemla.

Pahoran needed Moroni to bring his army and help him defeat those wicked people. Moroni and his men immediately prepared to join Pahoran's forces.

Moroni sent many of his men to the Nephite leaders nearby. These commanders needed all the help they could get, because the Lamanites continued to cause trouble.

Moroni and the rest of the soldiers marched as quickly as they could to the land of Gideon. As they passed through the countryside, more and more men joined them. These men wanted to remain free. They did not want a king to rule over them.

By the time Moroni reached the land of Gideon, he had thousands of soldiers willing to fight for the cause of freedom. Pahoran was delighted to see them.

Moroni and Pahoran led their forces into battle against the kingmen. The freemen fought so fiercely that the kingmen lost the battle.

Pahoran was once again the Chief Judge of Zarahemla. According to Nephite law, the kingmen were entitled to a trial. Pahoran made sure they got their chance to defend themselves against their accusers.

Pahoran asked each man if he was willing to fight for the freedom of his countrymen. If the man said yes, he was allowed to join the Nephite army. If the man said no, he was put to death.

Moroni rejoiced at the defeat of the kingmen, but he knew that his people still needed to defend themselves against the Lamanites. He was afraid that the war would last a long time.

He was right.

How did Moroni know that the war would continue?

What did he plan to do about it?

What would you do?

Complete the Picture

You saw this picture on page 193, but on this page parts of it are missing!
Can you fill in the missing sections?

Word Search

```
P R A W M N O W E S E T I H P E N P W K
O A P F L I V T Y Z L J O T F F A Q M N
V G D F T Y O W U I J S D I X H Z C O M
R E Q F R E E M E N J D J H O T R C R J
L E N O P L G O L H R A E R T Z Y B O U
W Q S G Z A R A H E M L A F S O G J N D
I X P M K G E V V H L N H S E H Q T I G
I A M T G E Q J B S Y O P S E N D P J E
P A B V U K L X E F Q Z O E B P D U V T
E J G J O V Q B L C T H L T A L W B I C
D F L L R P N S U M V N M I Z E E T D A
S C G W B X E V A O N K I N G H L N J K
H I T L V B I N F D R X H A K F C X Y C
B E X G P G A I X E D T P M I N Z L S G
P B L Y A V O N O E D I G A N O N C I J
Q E T T N X K R A R A F Y L G D Z C C Q
R K Z W D B S L B F B X K V M H Q R K Q
I B R Y Y F O I F P F B X O E D G D F A
G V C V N N T R X Z B V W J N I S Q L O
S Z Q I I O K V B W R X H A Y K D L T U
```

DEFEND

FREEDOM

FREEMEN

GIDEON

HELP

JUDGE

KING

KINGMEN

LAMANITES

MORONI

NEPHITES

PAHORAN

TROUBLE

WAR

ZARAHEMLA

The Still, Small Voice

Helaman 5-6

Nephi and Lehi were the sons of a prophet, whose name was also Nephi. Nephi and Lehi were more than just brothers; they were missionary companions.

After teaching the Nephites in Zarahemla, Nephi and Lehi travelled to the land of Nephi, where the Lamanites had lived since the first Lehi came to the American Continent.

These Lamanites were not happy to see Nephite missionaries. They arrested Nephi and Lehi and threw them in jail. This was the very same jail where Ammon and his brothers had stayed, many years earlier.

The poor men had no food for several days. The jail was cold and dark. They were cold, hungry, and slightly discouraged.

The Lamanite guards came to get Nephi and Lehi, so that they could be executed. But when the guards entered the prison, they saw a ring of fire around their Nephite prisoners!

The fire surrounded Nephi and Lehi, but it did not burn them. The guards were frightened. They did not understand what was happening.

Nephi and Lehi saw a golden opportunity to teach. They began to preach to the guards, teaching them about repentance and Jesus Christ. They stood there in the circle of fire and talked and talked to the stunned Lamanites.

One of the guards knew what was happening. He was a Nephite who had lived among the Lamanites for many years. His name was Aminidab. He had heard about this type of thing happening before.

When Nephi and Lehi were done talking, a cloud of darkness came into the room. No one could see anything. Then they all heard a voice in the darkness. The voice was soft and calm, but it seemed to go right through their bodies.

The voice said, "You need to repent! Do not try to hurt my servants! They are here to teach you and help you. They have good things to tell you."

The voice spoke three times. The Lamanites were so scared that they couldn't run. They just stood there, listening.

The guards saw a light shining through the cloud of darkness. The light shone on the faces of Nephi and Lehi. The two Nephites seemed to be talking to someone. Who were they talking to?

Aminidab answered this question. He said, "They are talking to angels."

The Lamanites asked him, "What do we need to do to get rid of this awful darkness?"

Aminidab said, "You need to repent. You need to pray until the Spirit of God gives you knowledge about Jesus Christ."

The guards did as he suggested. They began to pray. When they opened their eyes, they were surrounded by the circle of fire, too!

Again they heard the still, small voice. It said, "Peace, peace be unto you because of your faith in my Son."

Many of the Lamanites in the land of Nephi joined the Church. They gave the Nephites back most of their cities.

The Lamanites prayed and learned and grew strong in the Gospel. They were a mighty people because they kept the commandments and Heavenly Father was pleased with them.

Whose was the "still, small voice"?

What happened when the Lamanites repented?

Why is this story important for you to know?

Look It Up!

Look up Helaman 5:46-48 to fill in the blanks. Then find those words in the Word Search on the next page.

46 And it came to pass that there came a _____ unto them, yea, a _____ voice, as if it were a _____, saying:

47 _____, peace be unto you, be-cause of your _____ in my _____ _____, who was from the _____

of the _____.

48 And now, when they heard this they _____ up their _____ as if to be-hold from whence the voice _____; and behold, they saw the _____ open; and _____ came _____ out of heaven and _____ unto them.

Word Search

```
P A N E N Q E U H K J N X H L L Q B J Y
L T G C S I E S G R C H Z T P W O A J G
T P L E A S A N T W W O R L D T D F E D
W H I S P E R S D E R E T S I N I M Q J
U U E N Y L A R E F D H D O W N T X L W
B V F N V C N Y W E L L B E L O V E D Z
Q Q G O F O E F D O Z F A Q J X F Z S K
O Y N T C S I I B Y Y M X O V F T F A Q
S N F R V W H C A C I X A R C F M X X E
N S A J S K F F E K U J W A V O D L B U
E P A N G E L S F P H V U L U U D L Q V
V E U J R O Z G R L N P Q Y U N L X X V
A W Z S L M W L L J V R Y V X D T O L A
E S X U E H N O K W O P J U C A B F M H
H U S G I C P T L V K R F E E T F X U K
E O N S V W A L D B L K A G H I H Z B T
J F W U P A L E A K G G I D H O W E B H
I S N H E M A C P C K N T G M N M V P T
Z N J E Q Q V D F T Q J H X J L L A E P
F D I O X D V G Q A B Q I M Y G M V A Y
```

Samuel's Warning

Helaman 13-16

At this time, several years before Jesus was born, the Lamanites were more righteous than the Nephites. The Lamanites tried hard to make good choices. They prayed for the Lord's help in all decisions. They lived the Gospel as well as they could, and Heavenly Father blessed them.

The Nephites, on the other hand, slid down into wickedness. They began making selfish choices which made the people around them unhappy. One bad decision led to another, and pretty soon the Nephites were fighting each other again. Robberies, fights, and murders happened regularly in the Nephite cities.

One day, a Lamanite came to Zarahemla. His name was Samuel, and he was a prophet sent by Heavenly Father to teach the Nephites. When he tried to speak to them, however, the Nephites did not want to hear what he had to say. They threw him out of the city.

Discouraged, Samuel started the journey back to his own land. As he walked along, the Lord spoke to him and told him to go back again to teach the people in Zarahemla.

This time the Nephites did not even let him inside the city gates. Samuel knew that he needed to talk to these people, but how could he do it when he couldn't even get inside the gates?

Then he had an idea. He climbed the city wall. When he reached the top, he spread his arms and talked in a loud voice to the startled people below.

He said, "God has sent me to give you a warning. He says that if you do not repent, you will be destroyed."

The Nephites did not believe him. He tried to convince them by telling them when it would happen. He said, "If you don't repent, the Nephite nation will be destroyed completely before four hundred years pass." Four hundred years is a long time. The Nephites refused to pay attention to Samuel's words.

The Nephites were being foolish. In fact, they were being stubborn and

stupid. They knew how they should live, and they knew that God always keeps His promises. They knew that they should take Samuel's words seriously, but they didn't want to change.

Samuel talked to the crowd for a long time, trying to teach them about the Gospel. He said, "In just five years, Jesus will be born. When that happens, there will be three days without nights. The sun will set, but there will still be daylight. A new star will shine, brighter than any other."

The Nephites were tired of listening to this man. Who was he, a Lamanite, to tell them what to do? They called soldiers to get rid of the noisy man.

The Nephite soldiers shot arrows at Samuel, who kept talking. The arrows never hit him, even though the soldiers were very good shots. Soon it became obvious that the arrows

could not hit Samuel, no matter how skilled the soldiers were.

The Nephites grabbed stones and threw them at Samuel. The stones never hit him, either.

When the crowd saw that they could not get rid of Samuel, they called to the soldiers, "Arrest that man! Tie him up and throw him in prison!"

The soldiers climbed onto the wall and tried to capture the Lamanite prophet. But Samuel jumped off the wall and ran away. He was never seen by the Nephites again.

Some of the Nephites believed what Samuel was saying. Nephi taught them about the Gospel. Many of them were baptized and started to make righteous decisions.

Most of the Nephites, however, stayed just as they were. They continued being nasty and mean to each other and everyone else. They refused to listen to the words of God.

Why were the Nephites so mad at Samuel?

Why couldn't the rocks and arrows hit him?

Complete the Picture

Can you complete the picture? One half is drawn for you.

New Hope

Helaman 16, 3 Nephi 1

The people didn't listen to Samuel. At least, most of them didn't. A few listened, however. They went to Nephi, the prophet. They wanted him to teach them more about God.

These good people learned about the Gospel. They were baptized. They repented of their sins and tried to keep the commandments.

Some of the people who didn't believe Samuel decided that enough time had passed. They felt that the events that Samuel predicted should have already happened. They were happy that Samuel's words had not been fulfilled.

The faithful believers watched the heavens and prayed. They did not believe that the time for waiting was over. They prayed that the Savior would be born and that the rest of Samuel's prophecies would come true.

The unbelievers made a terrible law. They decided on a day when the prophecies must come true. If Samuel's words were not fulfilled by that day, all of the people who believed in Samuel would be put to death.

The day of death got closer and closer. Each night the sun set, just as it had every night of the peoples' lives.

Samuel had said that the sun would set when Jesus was born, but that the sky would not darken and there would be a day and a night and a day like one long day. However, each night when the sun set, the sky got dark as usual.

The people were frightened. Would they have to die? Should they believe Samuel? They felt that his words were true, but was it all worth dying for?

Nephi was very worried about his people. They had shown tremendous faith. They had done what the Lord had asked them to do. They had so much faith that they were willing to die for the truth, if they had to.

Nephi prayed and prayed. He prayed for an entire day. At the end of the day, a voice said to him, "Lift your

head and be of good cheer. The time is at hand, and on this night shall the sign be given." Christ would be born the very next day!

Nephi could hardly wait for the sun to set that night. He waited anxiously as the sun went lower and lower in the sky. Finally it disappeared altogether, and the sky never got dark. The prophecies were finally coming true!

Nephi and his people were very happy. In fact, they were more than just happy. They were relieved that their lives would be spared. They rejoiced that the prophecies were coming true. Most of all, they celebrated that their Savior was finally being born.

The unbelievers were astonished. Many of them were so shocked that they fell to ground as if they were dead. They knew that Samuel was right. They knew that they had been wicked.

All that night, it was as light as if it were the middle of the day. Samuel had said that on the next day, the Savior would be born. At the end of the night, the sun came up just as it had always risen. The light never changed. They knew that now the Savior had been born in Bethlehem.

That night, there was a new star in the sky. It shone brighter than all of the other stars. It was the star that led the shepherds and wise men to Bethlehem to see the new-born Christ. The people in the Americas, the Nephites and the Lamanites, looked at this star and remembered what Samuel had said. This star shone to tell the world that Jesus Christ had been born.

Many, many people repented and were baptized. The church grew strong as more and more people learned about the Gospel.

There were many people who didn't believe, however, and they were even more determined to cause trouble. As the years passed, the good people became more and more righteous, and the bad people became more and more unrighteous.

All of the adults at this time had actually experienced the night the Savior was born. Why did some of those people become unrighteous?

Why would those people continue to do bad things even though Samuel's prophecies had come true?

Reversals

Circle the answers to the questions below. This may be a little
more difficult than it appears, because the answers
are written backwards! Have fun!

Who prophesied that Jesus would be born?

amla   ihel   leumas   eerht lla

Nephi was worried that his people would be:

detacude   dezitpab   dellik

Nephi prayed for a:

yad elohw   rac wen   gnillac yramirp

The night Jesus was born, there was no:

ssenkrad   doof   ssenipah

The night Jesus was born, there was a new:

lamina   rats   esuoh   koob

Jesus was born in:

natsinahgfa   mehelhteb   ogacihc

Jesus' parents were:

lehte & derf   einre & treb   yram & hpesoj

A Widening Division

3 Nephi 2-3

As the years passed, the bad people caused as much trouble as possible for the good people. Many of the bad people formed a group called the "Gadianton Robbers". The Gadianton Robbers made secret plans to destroy the Church.

Both Nephites and Lamanites had joined the Church. They had to work together to defend themselves against the Gadianton Robbers. Finally, the Lamanite members decided to call themselves Nephites. From that time on, the name "Nephite" meant all of the people descended from the first Nephi along with members of other tribes who had joined the Church.

The Nephite community was ruled by a man named Lachoneus. He was smart. He knew that the Nephites had to think of new ways to defend themselves against the Gadianton Robbers. He gathered the Nephites together and made plans.

Lachoneus knew that only God could save the Nephites from the Gadianton Robbers. He told the people that they must keep the commandments so that the Lord could help them.

Then he made every family gather together all of their belongings and move into the center of the city. He placed guards around the city to protect the people. They built high walls, made weapons, and got ready for war. Many thousands of Nephites gathered in the city, with all of their animals and supplies. It was crowded, but it was safe.

Soon the Gadianton Robbers came. When they arrived, they found that all of the farms were empty. There were no animals. There were no crops in the fields. There were houses, but no food was in them. The Robbers needed to feed themselves, and they had planned to steal food from the Nephites. But the Nephites had taken all of the food into the city.

The Robbers didn't know what to do. They couldn't raise crops, because if they were working in the fields, they couldn't defend themselves. Also, they would starve to death before the crops grew large enough to produce food. There were no wild animals in the forests nearby. The Robbers were far, far from their homes. It would take so long to walk home that they would starve before they could get there.

The Gadianton Robbers were desperate. They had no choice but to attack the city. It was a terrible, bloody war. So many people died that the scriptures say, "there never was known so great a slaughter among all the people of Lehi since he left Jerusalem."

The Nephites won the battle. They took thousands of prisoners. Thousands of Lamanites were killed during the battle.

The Nephites fell to their knees and thanked their God for saving them. They knew that only God could have won that battle. God had spared their lives.

_____

What smart things did Lachoneus do?

Why couldn't the Gadianton Robbers go home to get more food?

Why did the Gadianton Robbers have to attack the Nephites?

Why did the Nephites win the battle?

Word Search

```
V C D I D K Y A K A E E N J T
W Q E D B U F G I T X G S V H
I Z S E B A B P S H K C T Y A
G W T Q R K D P U F N U S K N
E O R K R W I X S B L X E S K
U C O X O V L V U Z K F T R S
L D Y Z F I I P E S E K I E E
N Y E G A D I A N T O N H B F
L E H I T N K G O M X G P B W
S A B W R V G Y H D R F E O W
L I F R A M E M C R M U N R L
E T W V M C T V A C H U R C H
M C W Z S A C C L C B E Q S K
H G O F S K W V T L V O Y E E
R Z D I J H I N D M F N U B M
```

LACHONEUS
GADIANTON
ROBBERS
LEHI
NEPHITES

THANKS
SMART
CHURCH
DESTROY

Crossword Puzzle

SAFE

WALLS

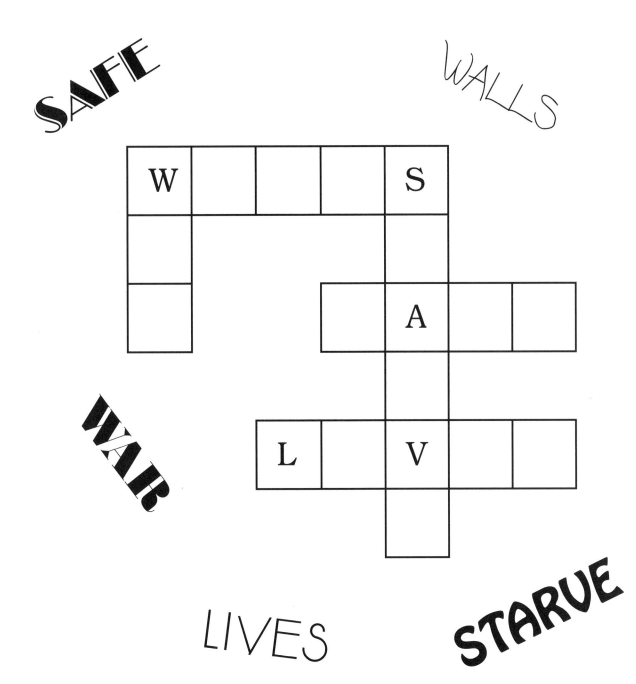

WAR

LIVES

STARVE

Downturn

3 Nephi 6-7

Many years had passed since the first of Samuel's prophecies had come true. The Gadianton Robbers had been destroyed. There was peace in all the land. The Church grew strong. The people became wealthy. However, when people become wealthy, many times it leads them to put other things before God and they become proud in their hearts and forget Him.

Some of the people had more money than others. They were able to go to good schools. They had fine clothes. They began to think that they were better than the people who had less money.

The people who had lots of money began to be powerful. They made the poorer people serve them. They were quite mean to the poor people.

As the next few years passed, the wealthy people became more powerful and more wealthy. The poor people got poorer and poorer. They were very unhappy.

As the people fought each other, they stopped listening to the prophets. The Church no longer existed in most of the cities. Only a few Lamanites remained faithful.

Nephi worked and worked to get people to listen. Angels came every day to help him. His brother was killed by the wicked Nephites and Nephi, by the power of God, raised him from the dead.

By the power of God, Nephi healed the sick, helped the blind to see, and made crippled people able to walk. It was a wonderful time for the righteous people who were willing to see the miracles that were happening.

The Nephite leaders were angry at Nephi, because he had more power than they had. They could not do the kinds of miracles that he could do. They wanted to kill him, but Heavenly Father protected him so that they were unable to harm him.

Thirty-three years had passed since the night of no darkness. The people had not forgotten that night or the strange star that shone during the next night. A long time had passed since then, and they were impatient for the rest of Samuel's prophecies to come true.

Many of the people believed that the rest of the prophecies would never come true. They no longer believed the prophets.

What miracles did Nephi do? How was he able to do them?

Why did the Nephite leaders hate him?

Why didn't the people believe that the prophecies would come true?

Look It Up!

Look up 3 Nephi 7:18-19 and fill in the blanks. Then use the words you wrote for the activity on page 217. Who is the scripture about?

18 And it came to pass that they were _____ with him, even because he had _____ _____ than they, for it were not possible that they could _____ his _____, for so great was his _____ on the Lord _____ _____ that _____ did _____ unto him _____.

19 And in the _____ of _____ did he _____ out _____ and unclean _____; and even his _____ did he _____ from the _____, after he had been _____ and suffered death by the _____.

Your Turn

Use the words from page 216 to make your own word search.
Give it to a friend and see if they can do it!

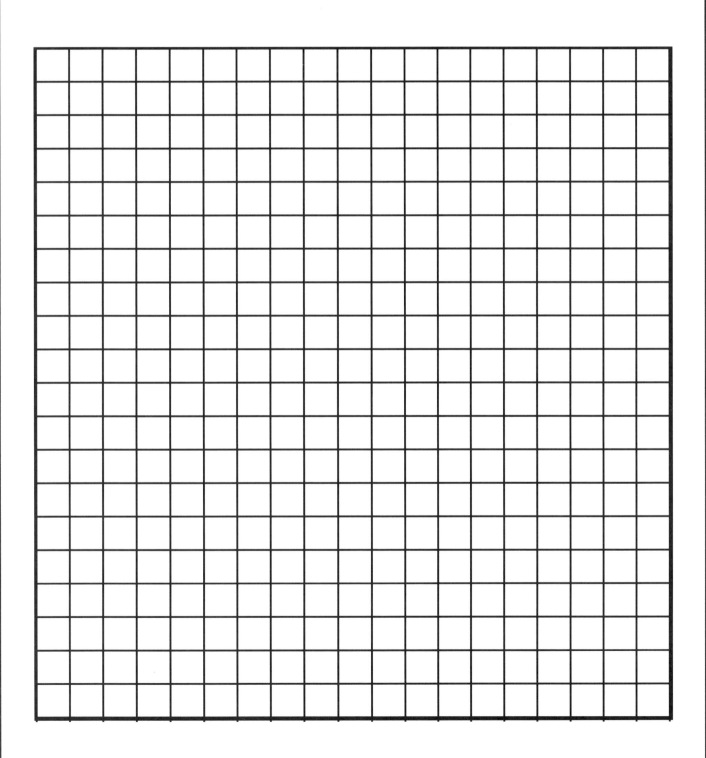

The Storm Hits

3 Nephi 8

One day, there was a terrible storm in the land of the Nephites. The wind blew fiercely, and lightning flashed again and again. The thunder was so loud, it seemed to shake the earth. No one had ever seen a storm like this one, and everyone was frightened.

The lightning caused fires in the great city of Zarahemla. Pretty soon, the entire city was on fire! Zarahemla was completely destroyed.

Earthquakes began to shake the earth. The city of Moroni fell into the sea. Everyone in that city drowned.

There was a landslide which completely covered the city of Moronihah. In fact, so much earth covered it that it looked like a mountain had covered it.

There were so many earthquakes, landslides, floods, fires, tornadoes, and other types of damage that the whole land had changed. Nothing looked like it had before.

Most earthquakes last for only a few minutes. An earthquake that lasts for three minutes can easily kill thousands of people. These earthquakes lasted for THREE HOURS! Just imagine how much damage was done!

The people who were still alive were terrified. The storms and earthquakes were causing the entire country to change. It must have seemed like nothing could ever be worse than that.

However, it did get worse. Darkness fell over the earth. It was a thick darkness that felt like a mist when it touched their faces. They tried to light fires, but the fires wouldn't burn. They used dry firewood and the best kindling and tried again and again to light fires. They tried to light candles and torches, but nothing would catch on fire.

The darkness was so thick that even the night sky was dark. The moon and stars did not shine. There was no light at all. The people could hear each other, but they couldn't see anything at all.

The darkness lasted for three whole days! The people were more scared than they ever thought they could be. They knew that many, many people were hurt and dying. They knew that many cities had been destroyed. They did not know what would happen next. Nothing could be heard except for weeping and mourning.

_____

Why did the earthquakes, storms, and darkness happen?

Did this fulfill any prophecies?

Who made those prophecies?

Secret Message

Why did Jesus come to earth? 3 Nephi 9:20-22 gives two reasons.
Find out what they are by separating the two kinds of letters.
The thin letters spell out the first reason, and the thick letters
spell out the second.

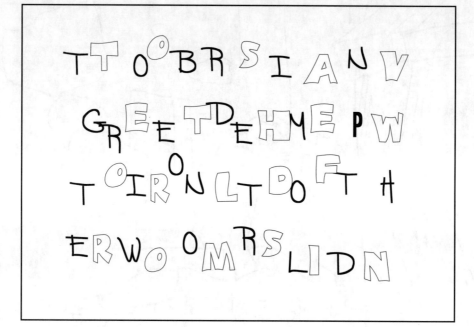

1. ___ ___ ___ ___ ___ ___ ___

   ___ ___ ___ ___ ___ ___ ___ ___ ___ ___ ___ ___

   ___ ___ ___ ___ ___ ___ ___ ___.

2. ___ ___ ___ ___ ___ ___ ___ ___ ___

   ___ ___ ___ ___ ___ ___ ___ ___ ___ ___ ___.

Matching Game

Samuel the Lamanite made many prophecies. Some of them
are listed below. Match the prophecy to the scripture

Jesus will be born.	3 Nephi 8:12-15
The night Jesus is born, there will be no darkness.	3 Nephi 1:17
The night Jesus is born, there will be a new star.	3 Nephi 8:20-23
When Jesus dies, there will be three days of darkness.	3 Nephi 8:9-10 3 Nephi 9:4-5, 8
When Jesus dies, there will be thunder and lightning.	3 Nephi 1:19
When Jesus dies, there will be earthquakes.	3 Nephi 1:21
When Jesus dies, mountains will become valleys, and valleys will become mountains.	3 Nephi 8:5-7

221

The Calm after the Storm

3 Nephi 11

The sun rose on the fourth day. The land was quiet. The people stopped crying and feeling sorry for themselves. The more they thought about what had happened, the more they realized that they should be happy, not sad.

After all, they had been a part of the greatest miracle ever to happen on the earth: They had heard with their own ears the voice of Jesus Christ. They had seen with their own eyes the fulfilling of the words of the prophets. They were still alive and experiencing the greatest event that had ever happened!

The air filled with the sound of people rejoicing and praying. The people gave thanks to Heavenly Father for allowing them to be part of this wonderful event. They rejoiced that they had listened to the words of Samuel. They had kept the commandments, and Heavenly Father had spared their lives.

A large group of 2500 people gathered at the temple in the land Bountiful. They told each other about their experiences. They marveled at the changes which had taken place in the land. Nothing looked like it had before, and that alone was enough to keep people talking for a long time. When Christ's words were added to the conversation, the discussion became even more lively. In short, the people had LOTS to tell each other.

While they were talking, they heard a soft voice speaking. It seemed to come out of the sky. The people looked around, but they couldn't see who was talking. Also, they couldn't quite understand the words being spoken.

The voice came again. It was a soft, sweet, calm voice. The scriptures say that it "did pierce them to the very soul, and did cause their hearts to burn." The people tried to hear what it was saying, but they couldn't understand the words.

The voice spoke a third time. This time, the people listened with the Spirit. They opened their ears and hearts toward Heavenly Father and asked for His help to understand.

This time, they understood the words. They looked up, because the voice came from the heavens.

This is what they heard: "Behold my Beloved Son, in whom I am well pleased, in whom I have glorified my name--hear ye him."

The astonished people saw a man coming down from the sky! He wore a white robe. He floated down, down, until he stood on the ground in the middle of the crowd.

Everyone's eyes turned toward the newcomer. No one spoke. They thought an angel had appeared to them.

The man stretched out his arm toward the people. He said, "Behold, I am Jesus Christ, whom the prophets testified shall come into the world."

When the people heard these words, they fell to the ground. They were overcome by the Spirit. They were astonished at what was happening. They were seeing Jesus Christ, whose birth and death had been prophesied by the prophets for so many, many years!

Jesus said, "Arise and come forth unto me, that ye may thrust your hands into my side, and also that ye may feel the prints of the nails in my hands and in my feet, that ye may know that I am the God of Israel, and the God of the whole earth, and have been slain for the sins of the world."

The people crowded around Jesus. Each person wanted to touch Jesus' hands and side, to see for themselves that he had been crucified and had risen again. One by one, each person touched the hands of Jesus. One by one, each person saw for himself that the prophecies had come true, and Jesus had been resurrected.

When each person had seen the scars on Jesus' body, the crowd cried out, "Hosanna! Blessed be the name of the Most High God!"

The people knelt before Jesus and worshipped him. They were thankful for all He had done for them and for the rest of mankind. He was Jesus Christ! They had seen and touched Him. What a marvelous time to be alive!

_____

What was the soft voice?

What did the voice say?

Who was talking?

Why did Jesus appear to the people on the American Continent?

224

Maze

This maze is a little different: it has a secret message! As you solve the maze, collect the letters along the path. When you are done, you will be able to read the message. What does it say?

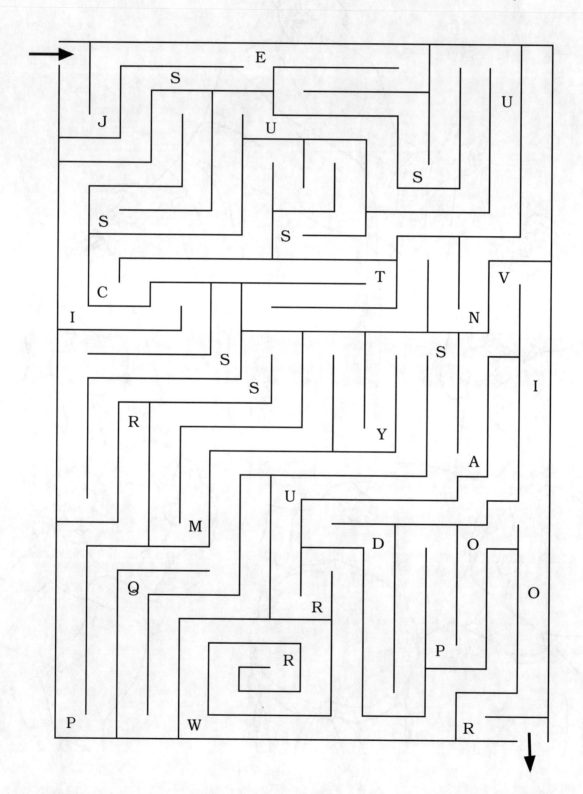

The Sermon on the Mount

3 Nephi 11-17

Jesus called for Nephi, the prophet. Nephi came forward and knelt at Jesus' feet. Jesus told him to stand up, and he did.

Jesus said, "I give unto you power that ye shall baptize this people when I am again ascended into heaven."

Then Jesus called forward twelve other men. He gave these men power to baptize, also. There were many, many people who needed baptism, and Nephi was going to need help.

After he called Nephi's twelve helpers, or disciples, Jesus taught the people some of the important lessons that He had taught to the Jews in Israel.

He taught them that when we are baptized with water, we can then be baptized "with fire and with the Holy Ghost". In other words, we can receive the gift of the Holy Ghost. Through Him, we can learn many important truths.

Then Jesus taught the Nephites the great sermon called in the New Testament the "Sermon on the Mount." This is one of Jesus' most famous speeches in the Bible. It is one of the most important things Jesus taught to the Jews, so He taught it to the Nephites, too.

He said, "Blessed are the poor in spirit who come unto me, for theirs is the kingdom of heaven.

"And again, blessed are all they that mourn, for they shall be comforted.

"And blessed are the meek, for they shall inherit the earth.

"And blessed are all they who do hunger and thirst after righteousness, for they shall be filled with the Holy Ghost.

"And blessed are the merciful, for they shall obtain mercy.

"And blessed are all the pure in heart, for they shall see God.

"And blessed are ye when men shall revile you and persecute, and shall say all manner of evil against you falsely, for my sake;

"For ye shall have great joy and be exceedingly glad, for great shall be your reward in heaven; for so persecuted they the prophets who were before you."

How long does Sacrament Meeting last? Only an hour and a half. Does it seem like a long time or a short time? Sometimes learning can make us tired.

Jesus taught the people many great things. He talked for hours and hours. The Nephites had listened to for so long that they got very tired, but they didn't care. They wanted to stay with Jesus as long as they possibly could.

Jesus looked at the peoples' faces and saw that they were exhausted. He said, "Go ye unto your homes, and ponder upon the things which I have said, and ask of the Father, in my name, that ye may understand, and prepare your minds for the morrow, and I come unto you again."

The people didn't say anything, but their eyes filled with tears. They didn't want Jesus to leave. They wanted to hear more and more and more.

Why did the people want to hear more?

Why did they cry?

What important things did Jesus teach them?

Why would Jesus teach the same things that He had taught the Jews?

Crossword

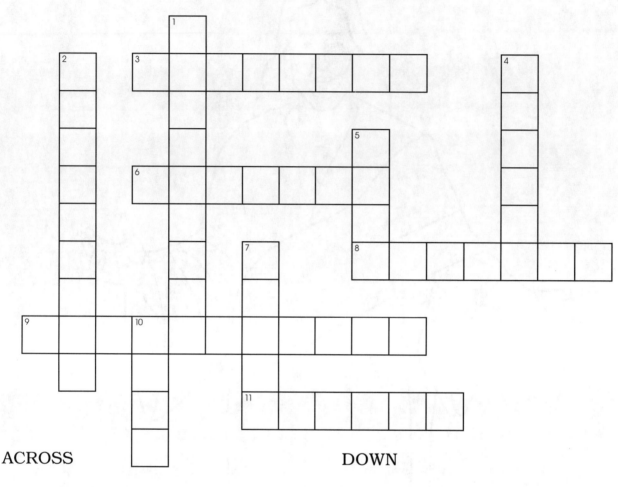

ACROSS

3. Blessed are the _____, for they shall obtain mercy.

6. Blessed are they who shall _____ in your words. . .

8. Blessed are the poor in spirit who come unto me, for theirs is the _____ of heaven.

9. Blessed are all the _____, for they shall be called the children of God.

11. Blessed are all they who do hunger and _____ after righteousness.

DOWN

1. Blessed are ye when men shall revile you and _____. . .

2. Blessed are all they that mourn, for they shall be _____.

4. Ye shall have great joy and be exceedingly glad, for great shall be your _____ in heaven. . .

5. Blessed are the _____, for they shall inherit the earth.

7. Blessed are the pure in _____.

10. Blessed are the poor in spirit who _____ unto me.

Miracles in America

3 Nephi 17

Jesus saw the peoples' tears. It made Him sad to see His people be so sad. He asked, "Have ye any that are sick among you? Bring them hither. . .and I will heal them, for I have compassion upon you."

What do you do when you are sick? What do you do if your legs or arms or eyes don't work properly? What do you if you break a bone? You go to the doctor, of course! What a silly question!

But what would you do if you didn't have a doctor? When this story happened, there were no doctors--at least, not the kind we have today.

There were healers, who used herbs to heal some illnesses. They could probably even set a broken leg so that it would heal correctly. But there were no X-Ray machines, no antibiotics, no stethoscopes, and no hospitals.

If you had a serious illness in those days, there was little anyone could do. As a result, there were a lot of people who were eager to be healed.

When Jesus asked if anyone was sick or crippled, there was great excitement among the people. The crowd rushed forward to bring their sick

children, friends, and relatives to be healed.

Jesus healed everyone who was sick. He helped crippled people walk again. He made blind ones able to see. He healed many, many people that day.

All of the people bowed down at His feet and worshipped Him. As many as possible came forward and kissed His feet. They were crying tears of happiness this time. The scriptures say that "they did bathe his feet with their tears."

What do you do if you get sick?

What would you do if you didn't have a doctor?

How would you feel if you were very, very ill and did not have any medicine to make you feel better?

How would you feel if someone came to town and made you better?

Word Search

```
C K U E X C I T E M E N T D V
A S C B V L L N P U W Y H Q I
M E Q S U F D D G P Z L K Y L
N E R I V C L E T F R V B Q O
A J L C D O C T O R C Q B U O
O V E K O U U K L O X L D D Q
D M J U S Q C R I P P L E D T
C O M P A S S I O N H N S B F
V N V L J A I H V B O Z E H H
H K J W I I V E V W S J O E C
E H G P N J G A O V P Y P A Z
A D K L B F F L O R I K M R U
L K S L R W I E G T T L K Q K
J H S N U A N R T C A A F L F
Z H B A Q K N L N G L W G G P
```

SICK
HEAL
COMPASSION
DOCTOR
HEALER
HOSPITAL

CRIPPLED
EXCITEMENT
WALK
HEAR
SEE

Jesus Blesses the Children

3 Nephi 17

There were lots of little children in the crowd. Their parents had brought them to see Jesus. Wouldn't your parents take you to such a magnificent event?

Jesus asked the people to bring the children to Him. Soon He was surrounded by a large group of children.

Jesus asked everyone to kneel down. Then He also knelt and began to pray.

The prayer was very special. The things Jesus said during the prayer were so sacred, the prophets could not write them in a book that everyone would read. Nephi, the prophet at this time, said, "The eye hath never seen, neither hath the ear heard, before, so great and marvelous things as we saw and heard Jesus speak unto the Father."

Nephi also said, "No one can conceive of the joy which filled our souls at the time we heard him pray for us unto the Father."

Those are the words of someone who was there with Jesus when this happened. Jesus was praying for him and the others with him. Can you imagine what that was like? Jesus knelt with them and prayed for them. No wonder their hearts filled with joy!

After the prayer, Jesus stood up. But the crowd of people were so overcome by the Spirit that they could not stand. Jesus spoke to them and told them to stand anyway.

The people had faith. They struggled to their feet. Jesus said, "Blessed are ye because of your faith. And now behold, my joy is full."

When He said those words, His eyes filled with tears. The people saw this and marveled at it.

Then Jesus gave each child a special blessing. He took the children one by one and blessed them and prayed for them.

Close your eyes for a moment and think what this must have been like. Can you imagine Jesus hugging you and putting His hands on your head? Can you imagine the weight of those strong, scarred, loving hands on your head? Can you imagine His voice as He prays over you? Can you feel the love He feels for you?

After blessing each child, Jesus' eyes again filled with tears. He said to the crowd, "Behold your little ones."

Nephi wrote, "And as they looked to behold they cast their eyes towards heaven, and they saw the heavens open, and they saw angels descending out of heaven as it were in the midst of fire; and they came down and encircled those little ones about, and they were encircled about with fire; and the angels did minister unto them.

"And the multitude did see and hear and bear record, and they know that their record is true for they all of them did see and hear, every man for himself; and they were in number about two thousand and five hundred souls; and they did consist of men, women, and children."

_____

What is your favorite part of this story?

Why?

What does this story teach you about Jesus' love for children?

Does He love you?

How do you know?

What Do You Think?

What did Jesus look like? This is how we think he looked.
Draw a picture of yourself sitting on Jesus' lap.
Close your eyes and try to imagine His arms
around you, giving you a great, big hug.

The Sacrament

3 Nephi 18

Jesus commanded His disciples to bring wine and bread to Him. While they were gone, He told the crowd to sit down. When the disciples came back with the wine and bread, Jesus taught the people about the Sacrament.

First He took the bread and broke it into little pieces. Then He blessed it. He gave the bread to the disciples and told them to eat some of it. Then He passed the bread to the people and commanded them to eat it.

He told them, "Behold there shall one be ordained among you, and to him will I give power that he shall break bread and bless it and give it unto the people of my church, unto all those who shall believe and be baptized in my name."

Jesus told them to always bless and share the bread as He had just taught them to do. He said, "And this shall ye do in remembrance of my body, which I have shown unto you. And it shall be a testimony unto the

Father that ye do always remember. And if ye do always remember me ye shall have my Spirit to be with you."

Next, Jesus passed a cup of wine to His disciples. Each drank a little of the wine. Then Jesus passed the wine to the rest of the people and commanded them to drink some of it. They did as they were commanded.

He said that they would be blessed for taking the sacrament, because it showed their willingness to obey Heavenly Father. He said, "Ye shall do it in remembrance of my blood, which I have shed for you, that ye may witness unto the Father that ye do always remember me. And if ye do always remember me ye shall have my Spirit to be with you."

_____

Why did Jesus promise blessings to those who took the Sacrament?

Why is the Sacrament important to you?

What blessings can you get if you take the Sacrament?

Make-A-Word

How many words can you make out of the letters in "Sacrament?"
We found eleven. How many can you make?

Sacrament

_____   _____

_____   _____

_____   _____

_____   _____

_____   _____

_____   _____

_____   _____

_____   _____

Learning to Pray

3 Nephi 19

After Jesus was finished teaching for the day, He took the hand of each of His disciples. He said that He needed to return to Heavenly Father for a while, but He would be back the next day to teach them more wonderful things.

Then He rose up into the air, higher and higher, until He "ascended into heaven". The people were covered with a bright cloud, but the disciples saw Him go up and later testified that they had seen Him ascend into heaven.

When they could no longer see Jesus, the people began to go back to their homes. They knew that Jesus would be back the next day. They had only one night to tell their friends and family to come and be taught.

All night long, the people invited their friends and family to come to see Jesus. They knew that this was the most important event that would ever happen in their lifetimes, and they wanted to share it with their loved ones. They worked all night long to spread the exciting news.

When the sun came up, there were so many people that Nephi and the disciples could not count them all. They divided the people into twelve groups, and each disciple taught one group.

The disciples had the people kneel down and pray. They reminded everyone to pray in the name of Jesus. First, each person repeated the prayer that Jesus had said the day before. Then each one prayed for the things that they needed.

Since each person had different needs, each prayer was different. But there was one thing that all of the people prayed for: the Holy Ghost. They had been promised that they could have the Holy Ghost to guide them if they kept the commandments, and they wanted this blessing most of all.

When they finished praying, the disciples went to the edge of a nearby body of water. The crowd followed them.

Nephi went down into the water and was baptized. When he came out of the water, he began to baptize his disciples. After the last one came up out of the water, they were "filled with the Holy Ghost and with fire."

In fact, Mormon says that "they were encircled about as if it were by fire; and it came down from heaven. . .and angels did come down out of heaven and did minister unto them."

While the angels were with Nephi and the disciples, Jesus came. He commanded everyone to kneel and pray. He went a little way from the crowd and knelt to pray. He asked Heavenly Father to bless the people.

As they prayed, the people's faces began to shine. The light shining from them grew brighter and brighter, until only brightness could be seen. All other colors disappeared, until the people looked as white as the whitest light possible. Jesus, too, was glowing white.

Jesus was impressed by the faith that the Nephites had demonstrated. He said, "So great faith have I never seen among all the Jews; wherefore I could not show unto them so great miracles, because of their unbelief."

He went on, "Verily I say unto you, there are none of them that have seen so great things as ye have seen; neither have they heard so great things as ye have heard."

The people had been rewarded for their obedience; Jesus had taught them many things that they would not have learned if they had not been so righteous.

_____

Nephi was a prophet. Why would a prophet need to be baptized?

How can you be "filled with fire" and still live?

What did Nephi mean by those words?

Why couldn't Jesus do the miracle for the Jews that He did for the Nephites?

What was the reward for the peoples' obedience?

How can you get similar rewards?

Count the Blessings

How many miracles did Jesus do while He visited the Nephites?
Read 3 Nephi 11-19 and list the miracles below.

1._____

2._____

3._____

4._____

5._____

6._____

7._____

8._____

9._____

10._____

You may find more than ten miracles.
List them on a separate piece of paper.

Bread & Wine

3 Nephi 20, 26

In the Bible, we learn about the many miracles Jesus performed for the Jews in Israel. In the Book of Mormon, we learn about the miracles He performed for the descendents of Jews on the American continent.

In the New Testament, Jesus made two loaves of bread and five small fish into enough food to feed five thousand people. In the Book of Mormon, Jesus did something similar.

During the second day He spent with the Nephites, Jesus asked the people to partake of the Sacrament. He broke the bread, said the prayer over it, and gave it to the disciples, who then passed it to the people.

This is the way Jesus did the Sacrament the day before, and we have seen it done many, many times in our own Sacrament meetings. But the incredible thing was that *no one had brought any bread to the gathering!* Jesus miraculously produced the bread for the Sacrament that day.

After the people had eaten the bread, it was time for the blessing on the wine. Again, no one had brought any wine with them-- Jesus again performed a miracle and produced wine for the Sacrament.

After the Sacrament, the people were filled with the Holy Ghost, "and they did cry out with one voice, and gave glory to Jesus, whom they both saw and heard."

After the Sacrament, Jesus taught the people. He talked for hours and hours. He quoted some of the prophets from the Old Testament and told the people to study their words.

Then Jesus healed the sick and the lame. He had done this the day before for the smaller group of Nephites, but this time there were so many people that it was impossible to count them all. There would have been a large number of people who needed to be healed.

_____

What other miracles did Jesus do for both the Jews and the Nephites?

Why did Jesus spend so much of His precious time teaching about prayer and the Sacrament?

Scripture Bread

What kind of bread did people eat when Jesus lived on earth? One kind is sometimes called "pita bread", and it is one of the world's oldest recipes. Look up the scriptures listed below to find the ingredients for this yummy recipe. Follow the directions and have lots of fun!

Ingredients:

3 1/2 cups 3 Nephi 18:18
1 1/4 cups warm 2 Nephi 22:3
2 tablespoons oil made from 1 Nephi 10:12
1 teaspoon 3 Nephi 12:13

Preparation:

Note: Your bread will be less authentic but will have a better texture and flavor if you add one package (1 tablespoon) of active dry yeast.

1. In a large mixing bowl, combine yeast with half of the 3 Nephi 18:18. Combine 2 Nephi 22:3, 3 Nephi 12:13, and oil. At this to the yeast mixture.

2. Beat the dough for several minutes with a large spoon. The longer you mix it, the better the texture will be.

3. Add the rest of the 3 Nephi 18:18 and knead the dough for a few more minutes. Again, the longer you knead it, the better your bread will be.

4. Put the dough into a greased bowl and let it rise for 45 minutes.

5. Punch the dough down and divide it into twelve equal pieces.

6. Roll each piece of dough into a ball, then roll it into a flat circle with a rolling pin. Let the circles rest for 20-30 minutes.

7. Have an adult help you preheat the oven to 400°.

8. Place each circle on a greased baking sheet and bake it for 10 minutes, or until it is lightly browned on the bottom.

9. When your bread is done, immediately put it into an airtight container for a few minutes. This will make it soft and easy to eat. Enjoy!

The Three Nephites

3 Nephi 28

Jesus spoke to His disciples one at a time and asked them what they wanted most of all. Nine of them said the same thing: after they died, they wanted to live with Jesus and Heavenly Father.

Jesus said to them, "Blessed are ye because ye desired this thing of me; therefore, after that ye are seventy and two years old ye shall come unto me in my kingdom; and with me ye shall find rest."

The nine disciples were happy because they knew that they would get their wish and live with Jesus some day.

Then Jesus turned to the three men who had not spoken yet. He asked them what they wanted most. They didn't say anything, because they didn't dare to tell Him what they really wanted.

But Jesus could read their minds. He said, "Behold, I know your thoughts, and ye have desired the thing which John, my beloved. . .desired of me."

John the Beloved was one of the apostles who served with Jesus while He lived in Judea. He was called "The Beloved" because Jesus loved him so much. Jesus promised him that he would never die, and that he would

be able to serve Heavenly Father until the last days.

This is what the three Nephite disciples wanted. They wanted to never die, so that they could do missionary work until Jesus returned in the last days.

Jesus told the three men, "Ye shall never taste of death; but ye shall live to behold all the doings of the Father unto the children of men. . ."

Then Jesus touched each of the nine disciples with His finger. He didn't touch the three who wanted to live forever.

Nephi wrote, "And behold, the heavens were opened, and they [the Three Nephites] were caught up into heaven, and saw and heard unspeakable things."

When the three men returned, they told the people that they had heard many wonderful things, but that they were not able to tell anyone what had happened to them or what they had been taught. They did say that their bodies had changed in some unexplainable way so that they could "behold the things of God."

These three special men had remarkable lives. They went throughout the

land, doing missionary work. Bad people threw them in prison, but the prisons broke open and the three Nephites were able to walk out.

People dug deep holes and threw the three disciples in them. But no matter how deep the holes were, Heavenly Father helped His missionaries escape.

Three times bad people threw them into furnaces. Each time, the disciples lived through the fires and were not hurt.

Twice, they were thrown into cages of wild animals. Both times the brave men played with the animals like a little child would play with a lamb.

The wild, fierce animals played with the men and did not hurt them.

Many, many years later they came to visit the prophet Mormon and ministered to him while he wrote the Book of Mormon. Mormon said that the Three Nephites will live until Jesus returns in the last days, so they are somewhere on the earth today! (Who knows, you may even have met them. Have you met any really especially wonderful people lately? Keep your eyes open!)

What happened to the three Nephites' bodies? Why?

Many wicked people tried to hurt them. Why weren't they ever injured?

Look It Up!

Look up 3 Nephi 28:7-9 and fill in the blanks. Then use the words you wrote to complete the puzzle on the next page.

7   Therefore, more (18)_____ are ye, for ye shall never (27)_____ of (3)_____, but ye shall (20)_____ to (7)_____ all the (13)_____ of the Father unto the (12)_____of men, even until all things shall be (1)_____ according to the will of the Father, when I shall come in my (19)_____ with the (14)_____ of (5)_____.

8   And ye shall never (17)_____ the (26)_____ of death; but when I shall come in my glory ye shall be (11)_____ in the (9)_____ of an (8)_____ from (4)_____ to (2)_____ ; and then shall ye be blessed in the (10)_____ of my (6)_____.

9   And again, ye shall not have pain while ye shall (22)_____ in the (21)_____, neither (15)_____ save it be for the (28)_____ of the world; and all this will I do because of the thing which ye have (16)_____ of me, for ye have desired that ye might bring the (24)_____ of men unto me, while the (23)_____ shall (25)_____.

Crossword

The Cycle Continues

4 Nephi

As the years passed, the Church of Christ grew and grew. All of the people who survived the storms and earthquakes were converted to the Gospel. They shared everything they had, so that there were no poor people and no rich people. Everyone had what they needed, and they were happy and contented.

Many, many miracles happened in those years. The disciples healed the sick, restored sight to the blind, and caused the deaf to hear again. They did all of these things in the name of Jesus, using the priesthood.

The people had a wonderful society that lived in peace and righteousness for almost two hundred years. The prophet Nephi said, "Surely there could not be a happier people among all the people who had been created by the hand of God."

However, as time passed and the people prospered, they began to forget that Heavenly Father had given them all that they had. They became proud of their fine clothes and beautiful homes. Some of them became very wealthy and refused to share with the poorer ones.

Two hundred years had passed in relative peace. The people who lived the Gospel were faithful. The people who weren't righteous, however, became more and more unfriendly toward the Church.

This is another example of the "Book of Mormon Cycle." Because the people were prosperous, they turned away from Heavenly Father.

_____

What are the steps in the "Book of Mormon cycle"?

Word Search

```
Z  L  D  E  T  N  E  T  N  O  C  G  V  M  M
D  G  W  N  X  V  L  D  E  V  I  V  R  U  S
O  G  F  V  U  Z  C  G  D  S  R  E  T  Z  O
H  U  V  B  Q  G  O  S  P  E  L  A  H  H  E
M  W  V  B  N  Z  P  I  I  U  A  L  J  D  V
Z  S  E  L  C  A  R  I  M  V  M  P  R  C  G
K  Q  J  O  Q  N  T  V  X  V  Y  Q  H  D  L
K  B  B  E  M  R  S  R  M  D  R  M  P  I  G
I  C  I  P  P  V  C  O  N  V  E  R  T  E  D
P  H  X  E  P  G  V  U  I  H  M  L  O  P  Y
O  R  H  A  P  P  Y  X  O  R  X  W  F  P  T
Z  I  X  H  C  R  U  H  C  O  M  Q  E  Q  S
S  S  A  I  J  M  X  H  H  S  I  F  L  E  S
W  T  L  A  Z  Y  L  D  N  V  L  X  K  K  B
Z  B  B  Q  Z  P  K  U  W  F  H  Y  E  A  Q
```

CHURCH	MIRACLES
CHRIST	HAPPY
SURVIVED	CONTENTED
CONVERTED	SELFISH
GOSPEL	LAZY

255

Mormon Takes Over

4 Nephi

There was a large group of people who formed a different church. These people didn't believe in Christ. After all, Jesus had come a long time ago, and they hadn't been alive to see Him. They didn't believe that he really was the Savior.

These people began to persecute the members of Christ's church. The disciples worked miracles and did missionary work, but the mean people still wouldn't believe.

The non-believers threw the twelve disciples into prison. The prison walls fell down and the disciples walked out. The non-believers put the disciples into hot furnaces and into dens of wild animals, but the disciples were not hurt. Heavenly Father protected them.

Another hundred years passed. The Nephites became more and more prosperous. They built enormous cities. They were very wealthy people. They were proud of their prosperity. They began to establish many churches, but these churches did not teach the gospel of Jesus Christ and many people turned away from God.

The Lamanites were not as wealthy. They hated the Nephites and blamed them for their problems. They taught their children to hate. They became a wicked, hateful people who no longer believed in God.

A man named Ammaron was the prophet at this time. He was in charge of writing the history of his people and the Church.

The Holy Ghost told Ammaron to hide the records that he had kept and all of the other plates which had been handed down from generation to generation. Ammaron obeyed. He hid the sacred books so that they would not be destroyed by the wicked people.

After he hid the plates, he went to visit a boy named Mormon. Mormon was ten years old. He had been taught to keep the commandments, and he did his best to be obedient.

Ammaron said to Mormon, "I perceive that thou art a sober child, and art quick to observe." He told Mormon where he had hid the plates and instructed the boy to wait until he turned twenty-four to retrieve them.

Mormon listened to Ammaron's words. He remembered where the plates were hidden. He waited patiently until he could go and find them.

Mormon was sixteen years old. He was so strong and smart that the Nephite leaders put him in charge of the Nephite army. He did his best to lead them to victory. Even though the Nephites were not righteous, he still loved them and tried to help them so that they would not be destroyed by the Lamanites.

Mormon noticed something that made him very sad: His people felt bad about what was happening, but they would not repent. They felt sorry for themselves and sad that so many people were wicked, but they did not feel sorrow for their own sins. The Lord still would not bless them, because they were not repentant.

The Lamanites attacked again and again. Many, many Nephites died in each battle. One by one, Nephite cities fell and were taken by the Lamanites. Soon the Lamanites had taken most of the Nephites' land.

Mormon could see that the Lamanites were getting closer and closer to his home. The Nephites ran away from the city. Mormon ran to a hill called Shim and hid in the cave where Ammaron had hidden the sacred records.

Mormon was tired of fighting. When the Nephites won a couple of battles, they began to boast about their "great strength" and made plans to invade the lands of the Lamanites and take vengeance. Mormon knew that God was not pleased and would not help them if they were the ones who attacked.

Mormon decided that he didn't want to be the leader of the Nephite army any more, so he resigned his commission.

He went back to his family and took care of them. He waited faithfully for the day that he could retrieve the sacred records from Shim.

Why did Ammoron have to hide the sacred records?

What were the records?

What were they written on?

Who wrote them?

Why were they so important?

258

Word Search

```
P C M M Q L Q E U O P M Z S E
M S J R O I V A S D E N S U U
D X G E M Z T M V Q V O I F I
S Y T I R E P S O R P V G N P
R O S R E V E I L E B N O N R
G K S E C A N R U F A R Z Q O
S P A M S T E P P V C W Q K S
D I S C I P L E S O J Z B I P
F H X L L A M A N I T E S N E
X J S C K M Y W M C P A X O R
G D E K C I W V E M C P Z R O
A U C B I B S D K R A N J O U
Y X S T K X U D X V D R V M S
O O Y U H A T E F U L I O F B
P Q A G M P S L A M I N A H
```

AMMARON
ANIMALS
DENS
DISCIPLES
FURNACES
HATEFUL

LAMANITES
MORONI
NON-BELIEVERS
PROSPERITY
PROSPEROUS
SAVIOR

260

The Battle of Cumorah

Mormon 2-6

Life was very difficult in the land of Nephi. The people were so wicked, the disciples stopped doing miracles. Bands of robbers roamed all over the countryside, robbing and killing anyone they found. The Nephites and Lamanites fought each other constantly.

Mormon saw that his people were losing the war, so he decided that the best way to help them was to leave his cave and lead their army once again. The Nephites were very happy to see him.

The war went on and on, year after year. So many Nephites had died that

Mormon was getting desperate. He thought and thought about what to do.

Finally, he came up with a plan. He wrote a letter to the Lamanite king asking him to bring his army to meet Mormon's army for one last battle.

Mormon gathered all of his soldiers in one place, near the hill called Cumorah. This area had several hills, lots of trees, and a couple of rivers nearby. The Nephites knew this part of the countryside very well, and they hoped to be able to use it to help them in the battle. They also hoped that if they all worked together, they might be able to defeat the Lamanites.

Mormon divided his forces into groups of ten thousand. There were twenty-four groups, so there were two hundred and forty thousand Nephite soldiers.

Then the Lamanites arrived. Wave after wave of Lamanite soldiers appeared on the horizon. The Nephites were afraid. Mormon said, "Every soul was filled with terror because of the greatness of their numbers."

The battle began. The Lamanites fought as fiercely as wild animals. They used swords, arrows, axes, and many other kinds of weapons. There were so many Lamanites that the Nephite soldiers couldn't defend themselves or their families.

Thousands and thousands of Nephites died in that horrible battle. By the time it was over, only twenty-four Nephites were left alive. Mormon was wounded, but he lived. His son, Moroni, also lived.

Mormon said, "And my soul was rent with anguish, because of the slain of my people, and I cried. . .If ye had not done this, ye would not have fallen. But behold, ye are fallen, and I mourn your loss."

Why did Mormon lead the Nephite army?

Why were the Lamanites fighting the Nephites? Why did they hate the Nephites?

Why were the Nephites killed?

Why didn't Heavenly Father save them?

Look It Up!

What did Mormon say after the battle of Cumorah? Look up Mormon 6:16-18 and fill in the blanks to find out. Then find the words you wrote in the Word Search.

```
C  G  S  C  S  R  B  Y  D  R  H  T  J  W  M
C  U  Q  C  D  S  E  L  P  O  E  P  S  C  D
M  B  H  E  K  X  L  S  H  P  S  S  I  E  R
Y  Z  M  X  K  V  W  U  J  N  H  O  P  F  E
O  M  V  U  S  G  B  S  R  R  Q  A  K  C  J
C  S  T  W  O  E  J  E  A  V  R  E  H  B  E
I  X  I  R  U  F  V  J  N  T  J  L  K  A  C
R  D  O  E  L  A  L  I  E  Y  H  N  N  S  T
F  X  L  N  H  I  I  D  E  C  J  Y  I  M  E
D  L  I  T  D  R  C  L  A  C  S  C  A  R  D
P  L  C  M  O  C  S  I  M  R  E  S  L  A  H
O  O  N  O  S  N  E  L  L  A  F  R  S  M  S
L  R  Z  U  S  G  P  N  D  M  G  X  M  O  I
V  D  D  V  O  X  J  T  S  X  T  Y  I  U  U
I  I  W  D  L  K  E  F  J  N  C  P  U  R  G
L  P  W  W  K  A  Z  N  E  P  O  U  Q  N  N
E  L  Z  D  O  M  T  R  H  P  B  P  Q  O  A
```

16 And my _____ was _____ with _____, because of the _____ of my _____, and I cried:

17 O ye _____ ones, how could ye have _____ from the ways of the _____! O ye fair ones, how could ye have _____ that _____, who stood with _____ _____ to _____ you!

18 Behold, if ye had not done this, ye would not have _____. But behold, ye are fallen, and I _____ your _____ .

The Promise

Mormon 8-10

The last story in the Book of Mormon was written by Moroni, the son of Mormon. The Lamanites searched all of the hills and valleys until they had found and killed all of the Nephites except for Moroni. They even killed Mormon.

Moroni was all alone. All of his family, his friends, and his countrymen were dead. He was the only Nephite left, and he had to keep moving from one hiding place to another so that the Lamanites would not kill him.

He knew, however, that he could not hide from them forever, so he knew that someday they would catch him and kill him. Then all of the Nephites would be gone.

What a hard life! How would it feel to be all alone and know that you must stay hidden or your enemies would take your life? But Moroni felt that God wanted him to remain alive long enough to write his testimony and hide the records so that they would be found and translated in some future time.

While he was hiding, Moroni wrote and wrote. His father, Mormon, had taken the records that their forefathers had kept and made their stories into one book. He wrote this book on thin sheets of gold. Moroni finished this important project.

When he was done with the records of his forefathers, he wrote down some of the speeches that his father, Mormon, had made.

In Moroni's final chapter, he bears his testimony to us, the people who would receive the Book of Mormon in the latter days.

This is where we find the famous "Book of Mormon Promise". Mormoni promises us that after we read the book, if we pray in faith about the truth of the Book of Mormon, Heavenly Father will give us a testimony by the power of the Holy Ghost that it is true.

What a wonderful promise! If we ask for an answer with faith in Jesus Christ, our Father in Heaven promises that He will tell us if the Book of Mormon is true.

When Moroni finished writing, he hid the golden plates and all of the other records in a cave in the hill Cumorah. He knew that he had done what the

Lord wanted him to do. He also knew that someday Heavenly Father would choose someone to find the sacred books and bring them forth to testify of Christ.

Has Heavenly Father made a promise to you?

What is that promise?

What do you have to do to find out if the Book of Mormon is true?

Why did Moroni hide the plates in the Hill Cumorah?

Why is this important to us?

Contract

I Will:

1. Read the Book of Mormon
2. Pray with faith in Jesus Christ

Heavenly Father will:

Tell me if the Book of Mormon is true, through the Holy Ghost

_____

signed

Put Your
Picture Here

Heavenly Father and Jesus Love Me!